English Names
of Wild Flowers

C000264841

A List Recommended by the Botanical
Society of the British Isles

EDITION TWO

JOHN G. DONY
Past President of the Botanical Society of the British Isles

STEPHEN L. JURY
Department of Botany, University of Reading

FRANKLYN PERRING
Royal Society for Nature Conservation

Computer-set and prepared at the Department
of Botany, University of Reading, for

THE BOTANICAL SOCIETY OF THE BRITISH ISLES

First published in 1974
Reprint (with corrections) 1980
Second edition 1986

ISBN 0 901158 15 1

Published by the Botanical Society of the
British Isles

A List of Recommended English Names for British Wild Plants

INTRODUCTION

The need to apply English names to wild plants is comparatively recent. Our ancestors were content originally to give such names only to plants for which they had a use, with the result that the English names of many of our trees date back to the Anglo-Saxon period. This may be seen in a number of place names: Aspley (Asplea in 969) was an aspen-tree clearing, Salford (Saleford in 1086) was a ford by sallows, etc. In the same manner plants which were edible received names which could vary from place to place. Whortleberry, bilberry, huckleberry, whorts and blaeberry were all applied to one species. Gorse and furze appear early, but could have had reference also to juniper, or any other quick-growing small bushes used for fuel. Although medieval documents contain abundant references to wild plants some doubt often remains as to their precise identity.

Some persistent weeds also received names which were local in their use. The various names applied to <u>Aegopodium</u> <u>podagraria</u> - Bishop's-weed, Pope's-weed, goutweed, Herb Gerard, ground-elder - illustrate the many appellations of a plant with which so many people have had direct contact.

The introduction of printing brought a measure of consistency with the use of English names for many wild plants by the herbalists. They found some names already widely used, but they were more often forced to invent names by translating those in Greek or Latin.

The early botanical works were in Latin, usually giving long names for plants which were in the nature of descriptions rather than simple names. The introduction of binomials by Linnaeus in his <u>Species Plantarum</u> (1753) brought not only stability to nomenclature but a remarkable increase in the study of plants. In the later years of the eighteenth century came the publication of the first Floras in English, bringing with them an increased need for English names of the plants to take their place side by side with the simplified Latin names. By this time most wild plants had English names, many too coarse and vulgar for use by young ladies who were being urged to take up the study of plants. Any names which were suitable, and generally accepted, were used but, as had been the case with the herbalists, the newer school of botanists had to resort to invention. This they often proceeded to do with a literal translation of the new Latin name into English. The English name frequently became a simple means of remembering the Latin name and vice versa. A plant with the specific name <u>latifolia</u> would carry the adjective 'broad-leaved' to its English name even if a closely allied species had leaves just as broad or even broader. It was, however, a good system and by the time of Bentham and Hooker's superb Flora (1887) it could well have appeared that a stable position had been reached in which each wild plant had its Latin name with a corresponding English name both of which would last for all time.

Time has undermined the stability of the Latin names as taxonomists have found that many names have been wrongly applied - what we had known for so long as <u>Scrophularia aquatica</u> must now be <u>S</u>. <u>auriculata</u>, to quote just one of many instances. The study of botany is not static and research has shown that many a large genus of plants could be better considered to consist of a number of smaller genera. Some smaller genera have been shown to constitute one large genus. In many instances these changes may be a matter of opinion but it is very necessary for the study of botany in the British Isles to be consistent with what is accepted elsewhere. In recent years what we may have known as dogwood or cornel or dog-berry or dogberry-tree has had almost as many Latin names in <u>Cornus sanguinea</u>, <u>Thelycrania sanguinea</u> and <u>Swida sanguinea</u>.

Authors of the Floras since Bentham and Hooker did not strictly adhere to the English names they used, having often good reasons for their individual departures. This produced a situation which was confusing enough to botanists but even more so to an increasing number, particularly those concerned with nature conservation, who claim no botanical knowledge, but need to apply an English name to a particular plant with some confidence, so that others will know to which species of plant they refer.

By the late 1960s it became clear to the Botanical Society of the British Isles that the only way of making progress towards stability of English Names would be the production of a list of recommended names for wild plants. It was with this in view that the council of the BSBI in 1968 appointed a Working Party consisting of two of us (JGD and FHP), with Catherine (Kit) M Rob, to prepare such a list. A preliminary list was prepared and circulated to members of the Council of the BSBI and others who had expressed an interest. Many suggestions and helpful criticisms were received, especially from D McClintock, R Chancellor of the Weed Research Organisation, who wisely insisted that the English names of weeds should be those known to farmers, and the late J E Lousley. Each list was carefully considered, enabling the final version to be published by Butterworths in 1974. This found wide acceptance not only by field botanists, but within the fields of nature conservation, agriculture and horticulture, and a reprint with a few corrections was published by the BSBI in 1980, Butterworths having relinquished their publication rights.

In the twelve years since the first list was published, there have been inevitable changes in nomenclature and taxonomy making a revised list desirable. Kit Rob, whose contribution had been so valuable, sadly died in 1975, and much of the organisation of the revision has been carried out in the Department of Botany, University of Reading by a new author (SLJ). In compiling this revised list we have been grateful for the helpful suggestions from a group of advisers including: J R Akeroyd, R M Burton, E J Clement, G G Graham, D H Kent, D McClintock, Miss M J P Scannell and C A Stace.

The list now published is based on the same principles as the original one and demands some explanation.

<u>One English name only for a species is adopted</u>. We considered carefully a number of instances in which two English names were used widely, e.g. ling and heather for <u>Calluna vulgaris</u>. Such apparently good cases were numerous. We decided finally that alternative names would cause confusion and contradict the requirement that the Working

Party recommend a separate name for each wild plant.

Inappropriate names are rejected. These are usually literal translations of Latin names which are not appropriate. We have preferred Broad-leaved Willowherb to Mountain Willowherb for _Epilobium montanum_ as this is not in Britain an exclusively montane species.

A binomial system is adopted. Some English names, e.g. holly, may stand in their own right, but in those cases where a number of closely allied species bear the same English generic name, e.g. vetch, we have strictly adhered to binomials. We have converted trinomials, which were often ambiguous, into binomials by using hyphens, and created 'English' sub-genera. The reader will find male-ferns, water-speedwells, etc., which we hope will eliminate such ambiguities as scaly male fern and blue water speedwell. In following this principle we are fully aware that ambiguities still remain with small-white orchid and early-purple orchid, but we have resisted the temptation to make sub-genera of white-orchids and purple-orchids, having in them only one species.

English generic names are limited to one family of plants. An application of this principle may be seen with the cabbages which we have limited to the Cruciferae. St Patrick's-cabbage is not a true cabbage as it belongs to the Saxifragaceae, and is in consequence hyphenated. We have made some exceptions to this rule.

1. Horse-radish although with the other radishes in the Cruciferae we consider far enough removed from them to stand in its own right.

2. White bryony and black bryony each stand alone as it is not clear whether the true bryony is _Bryonia_ (Cucurbitaceae) or _Tamus_ (Dioscoreaceae).

3. Greater celandine and lesser celandine each stand alone as it is not clear whether the true celandine is _Chelidonium_ (Papaveraceae) or _Ranunculus ficaria_ (Ranunculaceae).

4. Allseed and four-leaved allseed stand, as it is not clear whether _Radiola linoides_ (Linaceae) or _Polycarpon tetraphyllum_ (Caryophyllaceae) is the true allseed.

5. Fringed water-lily (_Nymphoides peltata_) has been included with the other water-lilies (_Nuphar_ and _Nymphaea_) although in a different family (Menyanthaceae), rather than create a 'genus' fringed-water-lily, with one species.

We have considered the true chestnut to be _Castanea_ (Fagaceae) and the true purslane to be _Portulaca_ (Portulaceae).

Plant names from other families forming part of a longer name are hyphenated. This follows the sub-generic principle and is seen most clearly amongst the 'water' plants, e.g. water-dropwort, water-lily, water-violet. We have adopted water-cress to show that this belongs to the bigger group of cresses, although watercress is now a common usage.

In following this principle, we have made a major exception in the grasses. We have applied 'rush' in its restricted sense to _Juncus_, and 'sedge' to _Carex_ (with _Kobresia simpliciuscula_ False Sedge as a sole exception), but find no genus to which 'grass' can be so restricted. We have, however, restricted 'grass' when used with a hyphen to the true grasses (Gramineae). We have made cottongrass one word, as the cottongrasses are not true grasses, and grass is used here as a general term. We experienced some difficulty with blue-eyed-grass and yellow-eyed-grass which might have been solved by making a genus of eyed-grasses, and by so doing making an exception to a principle which had worked well.

Otherwise multi-syllable words are unhyphenated unless a hyphen is needed to make the meaning clear. Thus we have hornbeam, whitebeam, longleaf and oysterplant, but thorow-wax and yellow-wort.

THE LIST

This is in two parts, Latin-English and English-Latin, both arranged in alphabetical order. We have tried to include names for all the species listed in the Excursion Flora of the British Isles, 3rd edition, by A R Clapham, T G Tutin and †E F Warburg (1981) with the notable exception of most microspecies in the genera Alchemilla, Euphrasia, Hieracium, Rubus, Sorbus and Taraxacum: on the other hand we have included a number of additional alien species which the advisory group has convinced us are so well and widely established that they should be recognised as part of the British flora. There can be no finality in these matters but the authors have resisted pleas to enlarge the book by adding all casuals and aliens for the benefit of a few, but at an increased cost to many.

The Latin name to English name list

This includes all Latin names as outlined above and synonyms to changes which have occurred since publication of the first edition. Furthermore, in this new edition, the authorities of the names have been added, so that this book by itself will serve the needs of those compiling or checking botanical texts.

The Latin names of the plants included are those in most general use now (1986), being mainly those adopted in the Excursion Flora of the British Isles, 3rd edition (1981). In addition, note has been taken of changes resulting from the revision of Flora Europaea Volume 1, currently being undertaken by the Flora Europaea editorial committee, largely at the University of Reading by J R Akeroyd, and in the preparation of a new Flora of the British Isles by C A Stace at the University of Leicester. However, recent changes proposed in research papers have generally not been accepted lest they represent temporary manifestations of taxonomic fashion.

The English to Latin name list

In addition to giving the recommended English name, this gives cross references to sub-generic English names and other closely connected English names.

The use of capital letters

These should be used always for the Latin generic names. For the English names we recommend that they be used as they are printed in the list for labels, captions to illustrations, notes on individual plants and lists of plants arranged in columns. In the text of articles, nature trail guides and lists of plants in running order we recommend that, with obvious exceptions, the capital letter should be dispensed with. We regret that we have not been able to give an indication of what these exceptions should be. It would be better to write: 'This is an oak-hornbeam wood with hazel coppice, a ground vegetation consisting of dog's mercury, hairy St John's-wort and wood anemone and with wide rides supporting two unusual brambles (<u>Rubus</u> <u>erraticus</u> Sudre and <u>R</u>. <u>griffithianus</u> Rogers)', rather than 'This is an Oak-Hornbeam wood with Hazel coppice, a ground vegetation consisting of Dog's Mercury, Hairy St John's-wort and Wood Anemone and with wide rides supporting two unusual Brambles (<u>Rubus</u> <u>erraticus</u> Sudre and <u>R</u>. <u>griffithianus</u> Rogers)'.

Changes from the lists of 1974 and 1980

The additional taxa included in this edition have increased its length by no more than 10%. Otherwise we have tried to conserve the English names used in earlier lists. However, our attention has been drawn to some inconsistencies which need correction, whilst there are a few other cases where taxonomic changes require the addition or alteration of names. Those concerned are:

1. <u>Agrostis</u> <u>canina</u>. The two subspecies <u>canina</u> and <u>montana</u> have now been given specific rank. Consequently <u>A</u>. <u>canina</u> (<u>A</u>. <u>canina</u> subsp. <u>canina</u>) previously known as brown bent has become violet bent, whilst <u>A</u>. <u>vinealis</u> (<u>A</u>. <u>canina</u> subsp. <u>montana</u>) assumes the name brown bent.

2. <u>Cicerbita</u>. The addition of <u>C</u>. <u>bourgaei</u> to the list has necessitated the creation of a new 'genus' blue-sow-thistle. Alpine sow-thistle has hence become alpine blue-sow-thistle and blue sow-thistle is common blue-sow-thistle.

3. <u>Myrica</u> <u>gale</u>. Bog myrtle was incorrect as myrtle belongs to the Myrtaceae not Myricaceae, so the correct English name is bog-myrtle.

4. <u>Petrorhagia</u> <u>nanteuilii</u>. It is clear that childling pink is a corruption of an original older name childing pink, which is now preferred.

5. <u>Physalis</u> <u>alkekengi</u>. This species was previously known as Cape-gooseberry but the authors agree this is totally unsuitable for a European species and now prefer the more descriptive Japanese-lantern. Cape-gooseberry is best used for <u>P</u>. <u>peruviana</u>, cultivated for its edible fruit.

6. <u>Robinia</u> <u>pseudacacia</u>. It is widely accepted that acacia should be reserved for species of the genus <u>Acacia</u>, therefore the name false-acacia is now preferred for <u>Robinia</u>.

7. <u>Trifolium</u> <u>ornithopodioides</u>. The name fenugreek should refer to the fodder and spice plant <u>Trigonella</u> <u>foenum-graecum</u> L. of Asiatic origin. Now that the former <u>Trigonella</u> <u>ornithopodioides</u> has been transferred to <u>Trifolium</u>, the name bird's-foot clover seems particularly appropriate.

We hope that some priority may be given to the names recommended here by authors generally, but especially those of local Floras, of articles intended for the general reader, of nature trail guides and of reports on sites such as nature reserves. At the same time we hope that regional and local names will long continue to be used but in a secondary and supplementary manner. We would much regret their passing and mainly for this reason prefer what is presented here to be a recommended rather than a standard list.

Not every wild plant name in this list is acceptable to each one of us collectively. We have given way individually to the pressure of each other's arguments and to the opinions of those whose judgements seemed more sound than our own. We hope that the list will go on being used in this spirit, and that it will help maintain some stability in a field that is constantly capable of offering a bewildering choice of apparently equally appropriate names.

ACKNOWLEDGEMENTS

We would like to thank Professor V H Heywood for the opportunity to use the computer facilities of the Department of Botany, University of Reading, which not only made the production of this edition much easier for the editors, but should ensure that future editions can be efficiently and rapidly prepared. We are particularly grateful to David Farmer who computer processed our data with such consummate skill.

J G Dony   March 1986
S L Jury
F H Perring

Acaena anserinifolia auct., non
    (J.R. & G. Forster) Druce <u>see</u> A.
    novae-zelandiae
    novae-zelandiae Kirk   Pirri-pirri-bur

Acanthus mollis L.   Bear's-breech

Acer campestre L.   Field Maple
    platanoides L.   Norway M.
    pseudoplatanus L.   Sycamore

Aceras anthropophorum (L.) Aiton   Man Orchid
    fil.

Achillea millefolium L.   Yarrow
    ptarmica L.   Sneezewort

Acinos arvensis (Lam.) Dandy   Basil Thyme

Aconitum anglicum Stapf <u>see</u> A.
    napellus
    napellus L.   Monk's-hood

Acorus calamus L.   Sweet-flag

Actaea spicata L.   Baneberry

Adiantum capillus-veneris L.   Maidenhair Fern

Adonis annua L.   Pheasant's-eye

Adoxa moschatellina L.   Moschatel

Aegopodium podagraria L.   Ground-elder

Aesculus hippocastanum L.   Horse-chestnut

Aethusa cynapium L.   Fool's Parsley

Agrimonia eupatoria L.   Agrimony
    odorata auct. <u>see</u> A. procera
    procera Wallr.   Fragrant A.

x Agropogon littoralis (Sm.) C.E.
    Hubbard   Perennial Beard-grass

Agropyron caninum (L.) Beauv.
    <u>see</u> Elymus caninus
    donianum F.B. White
    <u>see</u> Elymus caninus
    junceiforme (Á. & D. Löve) Á.& D.
      Löve <u>see</u> Elymus farctus
    pungens auct., non Roemer &
      Schultes <u>see</u> Elymus pycnanthus

1

Agropyron - continued
   repens (L.) Beauv. see Elymus
      repens

Agrostemma githago L.	Corncockle
Agrostis canina L.*	Velvet Bent
capillaris L.	Common B.
curtisii Kerguelen	Bristle B.
gigantea Roth	Black B.
semiverticillata (Forsskål) C. Chr.	
see Polypogon semiverticillatus	
setacea Curtis, non Vill. see A.	
curtisii	
stolonifera L.	Creeping B.
tenuis Sibth. see A. capillaris	
vinealis Schreber	Brown B.
Ailanthus altissima (Miller) Swingle	Tree-of-Heaven
Aira caryophyllea L.	Silver Hair-grass
praecox L.	Early H.
Ajuga chamaepitys (L.) Schreber	Ground-pine
pyramidalis L.	Pyramidal Bugle
reptans L.	Bugle
Alcea rosea L.	Hollyhock
Alchemilla alpina L.	Alpine Lady's-mantle
filicaulis Buser	Hairy L.
glabra Neygenf.	Smooth L.
vulgaris L.	Lady's-mantle
xanthochlora Rothm.	Intermediate L.
Alisma gramineum Lej.	Ribbon-leaved Water-plantain
lanceolatum With.	Narrow-leaved W.
plantago-aquatica L.	Water-plantain
Alliaria petiolata (Bieb.) Cavara & Grande	Garlic Mustard
Allium ampeloprasum L.	
subsp. ampeloprasum	Wild Leek
subsp. babingtonii (Borrer) Syme	Babington's L.
babingtonii Borrer see A. ampeloprasum subsp. babingtonii	
carinatum L.	Keeled Garlic
oleraceum L.	Field G.

---

* The two subspecies of A. canina have now been given specific rank:
A. canina subsp. canina is now A. canina and A. canina subsp.
montana (Hartm.) Hartm. is now A. vinealis.

Allium — continued
  paradoxum (Bieb.) G. Don   Few-flowered Leek
  roseum L.   Rosy Garlic
  schoenoprasum L.   Chives
  scorodoprasum L.   Sand Leek
  sphaerocephalon L.   Round-headed L.
  triquetrum L.   Three-cornered L.
  ursinum L.   Ramsons
  vineale L.   Wild Onion

Alnus glutinosa (L.) Gaertner   Alder
  incana (L.) Moench   Grey A.

Alopecurus aequalis Sobol.   Orange Foxtail
  alpinus Sm.   Alpine F.
  bulbosus Gouan   Bulbous F.
  geniculatus L.   Marsh F.
  myosuroides Hudson   Black-grass
  pratensis L.   Meadow Foxtail

Althaea hirsuta L.   Rough Marsh-mallow
  officinalis L.   Marsh-mallow
  rosea (L.) Cav. see Alcea rosea

Alyssum alyssoides (L.) L.   Small Alison

Amaranthus albus L.   White Amaranth
  hybridus L.   Green A.
  retroflexus L.   Common A.

Ambrosia artemisiifolia L.   Ragweed

Amelanchier confusa Hyl. see A.
    lamarckii
  grandiflora Rehder see A.
    lamarckii
  lamarckii Schroeder   Juneberry

Ammi majus L.   Bullwort

x Ammocalamagrostis baltica
    (Schrader) P. Fourn.   Purple Marram

Ammophila arenaria (L.) Link   Marram

Amsinckia lycopsoides (Lehm.) Lehm.   Fiddleneck

Anacamptis pyramidalis (L.) L.C.M.
    Richard   Pyramidal Orchid

Anagallis arvensis L.
  subsp. arvensis L.   Scarlet Pimpernel
  subsp. foemina (Miller) Schinz
      & Thell.   Blue P.
  foemina Miller see A. arvensis
    subsp. foemina

Anagallis - continued
  minima (L.) E.H.L. Krause   Chaffweed
  tenella (L.) L.   Bog Pimpernel

Anaphalis margaritacea (L.) Bentham   Pearly Everlasting

Anchusa arvensis (L.) Bieb.   Bugloss
  officinalis L.   Alkanet

Andromeda polifolia L.   Bog-rosemary

Anemone apennina L.   Blue Anemone
  nemorosa L.   Wood A.
  pulsatilla L. see Pulsatilla
    vulgaris
  ranunculoides L.   Yellow A.

Angelica archangelica L.   Garden Angelica
  sylvestris L.   Wild A.

Anisantha sterilis (L.) Nevski see
  Bromus sterilis

Anogramma leptophylla (L.) Link   Jersey Fern

Antennaria dioica (L.) Gaertner   Mountain Everlasting

Anthemis arvensis L.   Corn Chamomile
  cotula L.   Stinking C.
  nobilis L. see Chamaemelum nobile
  tinctoria L.   Yellow C.

Anthoxanthum aristatum Boiss.   Annual Vernal-grass
  odoratum L.   Sweet V.
  puelii Lecoq & Lamotte see A.
    aristatum

Anthriscus caucalis Bieb.   Bur Chervil
  cerefolium (L.) Hoffm.   Garden C.
  sylvestris (L.) Hoffm.   Cow Parsley

Anthyllis vulneraria L.   Kidney Vetch

Antirrhinum majus L.   Snapdragon
  orontium L. see Misopates orontium

Apera interrupta (L.) Beauv.   Dense Silky-bent
  spica-venti (L.) Beauv.   Loose S.

Aphanes arvensis L.   Parsley-piert
  microcarpa (Boiss. & Reuter) Rothm. Slender P.

Apium graveolens L.   Wild Celery
  inundatum (L.) Reichenb. fil.   Lesser Marshwort
  nodiflorum (L.) Lag.   Fool's Water-cress
  repens (Jacq.) Lag.   Creeping Marshwort

Aquilegia pyrenaica DC.	Pyrenean Columbine
vulgaris L.	Columbine
Arabidopsis thaliana (L.) Heynh.	Thale Cress
Arabis alpina L.	Alpine Rock-cress
brownii Jordan	Fringed R.
caucasica Schlecht.	Garden Arabis
glabra (L.) Bernh.	Tower Mustard
hirsuta (L.) Scop.	Hairy Rock-cress
scabra All. see A. stricta	
stricta Hudson	Bristol R.
turrita L.	Tower Cress
Arbutus unedo L.	Strawberry-tree
Arctium lappa L.	Greater Burdock
minus Bernh.	Lesser B.
Arctostaphylos alpinus (L.) Sprengel	Alpine Bearberry
uva-ursi (L.) Sprengel	Bearberry
Arctous alpinus (L.) Niedenzu see	
Arctostaphylos alpinus	
Aremonia agrimonoides (L.) DC.	Bastard Agrimony
Arenaria balearica L.	Mossy Sandwort
ciliata L. subsp. hibernica	
Ostenf. & O.C. Dahl.	Fringed S.
gothica see A. norvegica subsp.	
anglica	
leptoclados (Reichenb.) Guss.	Slender S.
norvegica Gunnerus	
subsp. anglica Halliday	English S.
subsp. norvegica	Arctic S.
serpyllifolia L.	Thyme-leaved S.
Aristolochia clematitis L.	Birthwort
Armeria alliacea (Cav.) Hoffmanns.	
& Link	Jersey Thrift
arenaria (Pers.) Schultes see A.	
alliacea	
maritima (Miller) Willd.	
subsp. maritima	Thrift
subsp. elongata (Hoffm.) Bonnier	Tall T.
plantaginea Willd. see A. alliacea	
Armoracia rusticana P. Gaertner, B.	
Meyer & Scherb.	Horse-radish
Arnoseris minima (L.) Schweigger &	
Koerte	Lamb's Succory
Arrhenatherum elatius (L.) J. & C. Presl	False Oat-grass

Artemisia absinthium

Artemisia absinthium L.	Wormwood
campestris L.	Field W.
maritima L.	Sea W.
norvegica Fries	Norwegian Mugwort
stelleriana Besser	Hoary M.
verlotiorum Lamotte	Chinese M.
vulgaris L.	Mugwort
Arum italicum Miller	Italian Lords-and-Ladies
maculatum L.	Lords-and-Ladies
Asarum europaeum L.	Asarabacca
Asparagus officinalis L.	
subsp. officinalis	Garden Asparagus
subsp. prostratus (Dumort.) E.F. Warburg	Wild A.
Asperugo procumbens L.	Madwort
Asperula cynanchica L.	Squinancywort
occidentalis Rouy	Dune S.
odorata L. see Galium odoratum	
taurina L.	Pink Woodruff
Asplenium adiantum-nigrum L.	Black Spleenwort
x alternifolium Wulfen	Alternate-leaved S.
billotii F.W. Schultz	Lanceolate S.
marinum L.	Sea S.
obovatum auct. see A. billotii	
onopteris L.	Irish S.
ruta-muraria L.	Wall-rue
septentrionale (L.) Hoffm.	Forked Spleenwort
trichomanes L.	Maidenhair S.
viride Hudson	Green S.
Aster linosyris (L.) Bernh.	Goldilocks Aster
novi-angliae L.	Hairy Michaelmas-daisy
novi-belgii L.	Michaelmas-daisy
tripolium L.	Sea Aster
Astragalus alpinus L.	Alpine Milk-vetch
danicus Retz.	Purple M.
glycyphyllos L.	Wild Liquorice
Astrantia major L.	Astrantia
Athyrium alpestre auctt. see A. distentifolium	
distentifolium Opiz	Alpine Lady-fern
filix-femina (L.) Roth	Lady-fern
Atriplex glabriuscula Edmonston	Babington's Orache
halimus L.	Shrubby O.
hastata auct., non L. see A. prostrata	
hortensis L.	Garden O.

6

Atriplex – continued
  laciniata L.   Frosted Orache
  littoralis L.   Grass-leaved O.
  longipes Drejer   Long-stalked O.
  patula L.   Common O.
  praecox Hulphers   Early O.
  prostrata DC.   Spear-leaved O.

Atropa belladonna L.   Deadly Nightshade

Avena fatua L.   Wild-oat
  ludoviciana Durieu see A.
    sterilis subsp. ludoviciana
  sativa L.   Oat
  sterilis L. subsp. ludoviciana
    (Durieu) Nyman   Winter Wild-oat
  strigosa Schreber   Bristle Oat

Avenula pratensis (L.) Dumort.   Meadow Oat-grass
  pubescens (Hudson) Dumort.   Downy O.

Azolla filiculoides Lam.   Water Fern

Baldellia ranunculoides (L.) Parl. Lesser Water-plantain

Ballota nigra L.   Black Horehound

Barbarea intermedia Boreau   Medium-flowered
                                     Winter-cress
  stricta Andrz.   Small-flowered W.
  verna (Miller) Ascherson   American W.
  vulgaris R. Br.   Winter-cress

Bartsia alpina L.   Alpine Bartsia

Bellis perennis L.   Daisy

Berberis vulgaris L.   Barberry

Berteroa incana (L.) DC.   Hoary Alison

Berula erecta (Hudson) Coville   Lesser Water-parsnip

Beta vulgaris L. subsp. maritima
    (L.) Arcangeli   Sea Beet

Betonica officinalis L. see Stachys
    officinalis

Betula nana L.   Dwarf Birch
  pendula Roth   Silver B.
  pubescens Ehrh.   Downy B.

Bidens cernua L.   Nodding Bur-marigold

Bidens - continued
  frondosa L.   Beggarticks
  tripartita L.   Trifid Bur-marigold

Blackstonia perfoliata (L.) Hudson   Yellow-wort

Blechnum spicant (L.) Roth   Hard Fern

Blysmus compressus (L.) Link   Flat-sedge
  rufus (Hudson) Link   Saltmarsh F.

Borago officinalis L.   Borage

Botrychium lunaria (L.) Swartz   Moonwort

Brachypodium pinnatum (L.) Beauv.   Tor-grass
  sylvaticum (Hudson) Beauv.   False Brome

Brassica napus L.   Rape
  nigra (L.) Koch   Black Mustard
  oleracea L.   Wild Cabbage
  rapa L.   Wild Turnip

Briza maxima L.   Great Quaking-grass
  media L.   Quaking-grass
  minor L.   Lesser Q.

Bromus arvensis L.   Field Brome
  benekenii (Lange) Trimen   Lesser Hairy-brome
  carinatus Hooker & Arnott   California Brome
  commutatus Schrader   Meadow B.
  diandrus Roth   Great B.
  erectus Hudson   Upright B.
  ferronii Mabille see B.
    hordeaceus subsp. ferronii
  hordeaceus L.
    subsp. ferronii (Mabille) P.M. Sm.   Least Soft-brome
    subsp. hordeaceus   Soft-brome
  inermis Leysser   Hungarian Brome
  interruptus (Hackel) Druce   Interrupted B.
  lepidus Holmberg   Slender Soft-brome
  madritensis L.   Compact Brome
  mollis L. see B. hordeaceus L.
    subsp. hordeaceus
  pseudosecalinus P.M. Sm.   Smith's B.
x pseudothominii P.M. Sm.   Lesser Soft-brome
  racemosus L.   Smooth Brome
  ramosus Hudson   Hairy-brome
  rigidus Roth   Ripgut Brome
  secalinus L.   Rye B.
  sterilis L.   Barren B.
  tectorum L.   Drooping B.
  thominii auct., non Hard. see B.
    x pseudothominii
  unioloides (Willd.) Beauv. see
    B. willdenowii

Bromus - continued
  willdenowii Kunth

Bryonia dioica Jacq.

Buddleja davidii Franchet

Bunias erucago L.
  orientalis L.

Bunium bulbocastanum L.

Bupleurum baldense Turra
  falcatum L.
  fruticosum L.
  lancifolium auct. see B. subovatum
  rotundifolium L.
  subovatum Link
  tenuissimum L.

Butomus umbellatus L.

Buxus sempervirens L.

Cakile maritima Scop.

Calamagrostis canescens (Weber) Roth
  epigejos (L.) Roth
  scotica (Druce) Druce
  stricta (Timm.) Koeler

Calamintha ascendens Jordan see
    C. sylvatica subsp. ascendens
  nepeta (L.) Savi
  sylvatica Bromf.
    subsp. ascendens (Jordan) P.W. Ball
    subsp. sylvatica

Calendula arvensis L.
  officinalis L.

Calla palustris L.

Callitriche autumnalis L. see
    C. hermaphroditica
  brutia Petagna

  hamulata Koch
  hermaphroditica L.
  intermedia Hoffm. see C. hamulata
  obtusangula Le Gall
  platycarpa Koch
  stagnalis Scop.
  truncata Guss.

Rescue Brome

White Bryony

Butterfly-bush

Southern Warty-cabbage
Warty-cabbage

Great Pignut

Small Hare's-ear
Sickle-leaved H.
Shrubby H.

Thorow-wax
False T.
Slender Hare's-ear

Flowering-rush

Box

Sea Rocket

Purple Small-reed
Wood S.
Scottish S.
Narrow S.

Lesser Calamint

Common C.
Wood C.

Field Marigold
Pot M.

Bog Arum

Pedunculate
      Water-starwort
Intermediate W.
Autumnal W.

Blunt-fruited W.
Various-leaved W.
Common W.
Short-leaved W.

9

<u>Calluna</u> <u>vulgaris</u>

Calluna vulgaris (L.) Hull	Heather
Caltha palustris L.	Marsh-marigold

Calystegia dahurica auct., non
    (Herbert) G. Don <u>see</u> C. sepium
  subsp. pulchra
 pulchra Brummitt & Heywood
  <u>see</u> C. sepium subsp. pulchra
 sepium (L.) R. Br.

subsp. pulchra (Brummitt	
& Heywood) Tutin	Hairy Bindweed
subsp. sepium	Hedge B.
subsp. silvatica (Kit.) Maire	Large B.

 silvatica <u>see</u> C. sepium
  subsp. <u>silvatica</u>

soldanella (L.) R. Br.	Sea B.
Camelina sativa (L.) Crantz	Gold-of-pleasure
Campanula glomerata L.	Clustered Bellflower
latifolia L.	Giant B.
medium L.	Canterbury-bells
patula L.	Spreading Bellflower
persicifolia L.	Peach-leaved B.
rapunculoides L.	Creeping B.
rapunculus L.	Rampion B.
rotundifolia L.	Harebell
trachelium L.	Nettle-leaved Bellflower
Cannabis sativa L.	Hemp
Capsella bursa-pastoris (L.)	
Medicus	Shepherd's-purse
Cardamine amara L.	Large Bitter-cress
bulbifera (L.) Crantz	Coralroot
flexuosa With.	Wavy Bitter-cress
hirsuta L.	Hairy B.
impatiens L.	Narrow-leaved B.
pratensis L.	Cuckooflower
Cardaminopsis petraea (L.) Hiitonen	Northern Rock-cress
Cardaria draba (L.) Desv.	Hoary Cress
Carduus acanthoides L.	Welted Thistle

  crispus auct., non L. <u>see</u>
    C. acanthoides

nutans L.	Musk T.
pycnocephalus L.	Plymouth T.
tenuiflorus Curtis	Slender T.
Carex acuta L.	Slender Tufted-sedge
acutiformis Ehrh.	Lesser Pond-sedge
appropinquata Schumacher	Fibrous Tussock-sedge

Carex - continued
aquatilis Wahlenb.	Water Sedge
arenaria L.	Sand S.
atrata L.	Black Alpine-sedge
atrofusca Schkuhr	Scorched A.
bigelowii Schweinitz	Stiff Sedge
binervis Sm.	Green-ribbed S.
buxbaumii Wahlenb.	Club S.
capillaris L.	Hair S.
caryophyllea Latourr.	Spring-sedge
chordorrhiza L. fil.	String Sedge
curta Good.	White S.
demissa Hornem.	Common Yellow-sedge
depauperata With.	Starved Wood-sedge
diandra Schrank	Lesser Tussock-sedge
digitata L.	Fingered Sedge
dioica L.	Dioecious S.
distans L.	Distant S.
disticha Hudson	Brown S.
divisa Hudson	Divided S.
divulsa Stokes	Grey S.
echinata Murray	Star S.
elata All.	Tufted-sedge
elongata L.	Elongated Sedge
ericetorum Poll.	Rare Spring-sedge
extensa Good.	Long-bracted Sedge
filiformis auct., non L. see	
C. tomentosa	
flacca Schreber	Glaucous S.
flava L.	Large Yellow-sedge
hirta L.	Hairy Sedge
hostiana DC.	Tawny S.
humilis Leysser	Dwarf S.
lachenalii Schkuhr	Hare's-foot S.
laevigata Sm.	Smooth-stalked S.
lasiocarpa Ehrh.	Slender S.
lepidocarpa Tausch	Long-stalked Yellow-sedge
limosa L.	Bog-sedge
magellanica Lam.	Tall B.
maritima Gunnerus	Curved Sedge
microglochin Wahlenb.	Bristle S.
montana L.	Soft-leaved S.
muricata L.	
subsp. lamprocarpa Čelak	Small-fruited Prickly-sedge
subsp. muricata	Large-fruited P.
nigra (L.) Reichard	Common Sedge
norvegica Retz	Close-headed Alpine-sedge
ornithopoda Willd.	Bird's-foot Sedge
otrubae Podp.	False Fox-sedge
ovalis Good.	Oval Sedge
pallescens L.	Pale S.
panicea L.	Carnation S.
paniculata L.	Greater Tussock-sedge
pauciflora Lightf.	Few-flowered Sedge
paupercula Michx see C. magellanica	
pendula Hudson	Pendulous Sedge

Carex pilulifera

Carex - continued
  pilulifera L.   Pill Sedge
  pseudocyperus L.   Cyperus S.
  pulicaris L.   Flea S.
  punctata Gaudin   Dotted S.
  rariflora (Wahlenb.) Sm.   Mountain Bog-sedge
  recta Boott   Estuarine Sedge
  remota L.   Remote S.
  riparia Curtis   Greater Pond-sedge
  rostrata Stokes   Bottle Sedge
  rupestris All.   Rock S.
  saxatilis L.   Russet S.
  saxatilis L. x vesicaria L.   Mountain Bladder-sedge
  serotina Mérat   Small-fruited
                                      Yellow-sedge
  spicata Hudson   Spiked Sedge
  stenolepis auct., non Less.
    see C. saxatilis x vesicaria
  strigosa Hudson   Thin-spiked Wood-sedge
  sylvatica Hudson   Wood-sedge
  tomentosa L.   Downy-fruited Sedge
  vaginata Tausch   Sheathed S.
  vesicaria L.   Bladder-sedge
  vulpina L.   True Fox-sedge

Carlina vulgaris L.   Carline Thistle

Carpinus betulus L.   Hornbeam

Carpobrotus acinaciformis auct.
    angl. see C. edulis var. rubescens
  edulis (L.) N.E. Br.
    var. edulis   Hottentot-fig
    var. rubescens Druce   Sally-my-handsome

Carum carvi L.   Caraway
  verticillatum (L.) Koch   Whorled C.

Castanea sativa Miller   Sweet Chestnut

Catabrosa aquatica (L.) Beauv.   Whorl-grass

Catapodium marinum (L.) Link see
    Desmazeria marina
  rigidum (L.) Link see Desmazeria
    rigida

Caucalis latifolia L. see Turgenia
    latifolia
  platycarpos L.   Small Bur-parsley

Centaurea aspera L.   Rough Star-thistle
  calcitrapa L.   Red S.
  cyanus L.   Cornflower
  diluta Aiton   Lesser Star-thistle
  jacea L.   Brown Knapweed
  montana L.   Perennial Cornflower

Centaurea - continued
  nemoralis Jordan   Slender Knapweed
  nigra L.   Common K.
  nigra L. subsp. nemoralis
    (Jordan) see C. nemoralis
  paniculata L.   Jersey K.
  scabiosa L.   Greater K.
  solstitialis L.   Yellow Star-thistle

Centaurium capitatum (Willd.) Borbás   Tufted Centaury
  erythraea Rafn   Common C.
  latifolium (Sm.) Druce   Broad-leaved C.
  littorale (D. Turner) Gilmour   Seaside C.
  portense (Brot.) Butcher see
    C. scilloides
  pulchellum (Swartz) Druce   Lesser C.
  scilloides (L. fil.) Samp.   Perennial C.
  tenuiflorum (Hoffmanns. & Link)
    Fritsch   Slender C.

Centranthus ruber (L.) DC.   Red Valerian

Centunculus minimus L. see
  Anagallis minima

Cephalanthera damasonium (Miller)
  Druce   White Helleborine
  longifolia (L.) Fritsch   Narrow-leaved H.
  rubra (L.) L.C.M. Richard   Red H.

Cerastium alpinum L.   Alpine Mouse-ear
  arcticum Lange
    subsp. arcticum   Arctic M.
    subsp. edmondstonii (H.C. Watson)
    Á.& D. Löve   Shetland M.
  arvense L.   Field M.
  atrovirens Bab. see C. diffusum
  brachypetalum Pers.   Grey M.
  cerastoides   Starwort M.
  diffusum Pers.   Sea M.
  fontanum Baumg.   Common M.
  glomeratum Thuill.   Sticky M.
  holosteoides Fries see C.
    fontanum subsp. glabrescens
  nigrescens H.C. Watson see C.
    arcticum subsp. edmonstonii
  pumilum Curtis   Dwarf M.
  semidecandrum L.   Little M.
  tetrandrum Curtis see C. diffusum
  tomentosum L.   Snow-in-summer

Ceratochloa carinata (Hooker & Arnott)
    Tutin see Bromus carinatus
  unioloides (Willd.) Beauv. see
    Bromus willldenowii

Ceratophyllum demersum

Ceratophyllum demersum L.	Rigid Hornwort
submersum L.	Soft H.
Ceterach officinarum DC.	Rustyback
Chaenorhinum minus (L.) Lange	Small Toadflax
Chaerophyllum aureum L.	Golden Chervil
temulentum L.	Rough C.
Chamaemelum nobile (L.) All.	Chamomile

Chamaenerion angustifolium (L.)
    Scop. see Chamerion angustifolium

Chamerion angustifolium (L.) J. Holub   Rosebay Willowherb

Chamaepericlymenum suecicum (L.)
    Ascherson & Graebner see
    Cornus suecica

Chamomilla recutita (L.) Rauschert
    see Matricaria recutita
  suaveolens (Pursh) Rydb. see
    Matricaria matricarioides

Cheiranthus cheiri L.	Wallflower
Chelidonium majus L.	Greater Celandine
Chenopodium album L.	Fat-hen
bonus-henricus L.	Good-King-Henry
botryodes Sm.	Saltmarsh Goosefoot
capitatum (L.) Ascherson	Strawberry-blite
ficifolium Sm.	Fig-leaved Goosefoot
glaucum L.	Oak-leaved G.
hybridum L.	Maple-leaved G.
murale L.	Nettle-leaved G.
opulifolium Koch & Ziz	Grey G.
polyspermum L.	Many-seeded G.
rubrum L.	Red G.
urbicum L.	Upright G.
vulvaria L.	Stinking G.

Cherleria sedoides L. see
    Minuartia sedoides

Chrysanthemum leucanthemum L. see
    Leucanthemum vulgare
  maximum Ramond see Leucanthemum maximum
  parthenium (L.) Bernh. see
    Tanacetum parthenium
  segetum L.   Corn Marigold

Chrysosplenium alternifolium L.   Alternate-leaved
                                        Golden-saxifrage

Chrysosplenium - continued
   oppositifolium L.

Opposite-leaved
   Golden-saxifrage

Cicendia filiformis (L.) Delarbre

Yellow Centaury

Cicerbita alpina (L.) Wallr.
   bourgaei (Boiss.) Beauverd
   macrophylla (Willd.) Wallr.

Alpine Blue-sow-thistle
Pontic B.
Common B.

Cichorium intybus L.

Chicory

Cicuta virosa L.

Cowbane

Circaea alpina L.

Alpine Enchanter's-
   nightshade
x intermedia Ehrh.
   lutetiana L.

Upland E.
Enchanter's-nightshade

Cirsium acaule Scop.
   acaulon see C. acaule
   arvense (L.) Scop.
   dissectum (L.) Hill
   eriophorum (L.) Scop.
   helenioides (L.) Hill
   heterophyllum (L.) Hill see C.
     helenioides
   oleraceum (L.) Scop.
   palustre (L.) Scop.
   tuberosum (L.) All.
   vulgare (Savi) Ten.

Dwarf Thistle

Creeping T.
Meadow T.
Woolly T.
Melancholy T.

Cabbage T.
Marsh T.
Tuberous T.
Spear T.

Cladium mariscus (L.) Pohl

Great Fen-sedge

Claytonia alsinoides Sims see
    Montia sibirica
   perfoliata Willd. see Montia
    perfoliata
   sibirica L. see Montia sibirica

Clematis vitalba L.

Traveller's-joy

Clinopodium vulgare L.

Wild Basil

Cochlearia alpina (Bab.) H.C. Watson
   anglica L.
   atlantica Pobed.
   danica L.
   islandica Pobed.
   micacea E.S. Marshall
   officinalis L.
   officinalis L. subsp. anglica
    see C. anglica
   pyrenaica DC.
   scotica Druce

Alpine Scurvygrass
English S.
Atlantic S.
Danish S.
Iceland S.
Mountain S.
Common S.

Pyrenean S.
Scottish S.

Coeloglossum viride (L.) Hartman

Frog Orchid

Colchicum autumnale

Colchicum autumnale L.	Meadow Saffron
Colutea arborescens L.	Bladder-senna
Conium maculatum L.	Hemlock
Conopodium majus (Gouan) Loret	Pignut
Conringia orientalis (L.) Dumort.	Hare's-ear Mustard
Consolida ambigua (L.) P.W. Ball & Heywood	Larkspur
Convallaria majalis L.	Lily-of-the-valley
Convolvulus arvensis L.	Field Bindweed

Conyza bonariensis (L.) Cronq.
see Erigeron bonariensis
canadensis (L.) Cronq. see
Erigeron canadensis

Corallorhiza trifida Chatel.	Coralroot Orchid
Coriandrum sativum L.	Coriander

Cornus sanguinea L. — Dogwood
sericea L. — Red-osier D.
stolonifera Michx see C. sericea
suecica L. — Dwarf Cornel

Coronilla varia L.	Crown Vetch

Coronopus didymus (L.) Sm. — Lesser Swine-cress
squamatus (Forsskål) Ascherson — Swine-cress

Corrigiola litoralis L.	Strapwort
Cortaderia selloana (J.A. & J.H. Schultes) Ascherson & Graebner	Pampas-grass

Corydalis claviculata (L.) DC. — Climbing Corydalis
lutea (L.) DC. — Yellow C.

Corylus avellana L.	Hazel
Corynephorus canescens (L.) Beauv.	Grey Hair-grass

Cotoneaster horizontalis Decne — Wall Cotoneaster
integerrimus Medicus — Wild C.
microphyllus Lindley — Small-leaved C.
simonsii Baker — Himalayan C.

Cotula coronopifolia L.	Buttonweed
Crambe maritima L.	Sea-kale

16

Crassula aquatica (L.) Schonl.   Pigmyweed
  helmsii (T. Kirk) Cockayne   New Zealand P.
  tillaea Lester-Garland   Mossy Stonecrop

Crataegus laevigata (Poiret) DC.   Midland Hawthorn
  monogyna Jacq.   Hawthorn
  oxyacantha Thuill. see C. laevigata

Crepis biennis L.   Rough Hawk's-beard
  capillaris (L.) Wallr.   Smooth H.
  foetida L.   Stinking H.
  mollis (Jacq.) Ascherson   Northern H.
  paludosa (L.) Moench   Marsh H.
  setosa Haller fil.   Bristly H.
  taraxacifolia Thuill. see C.
    vesicaria subsp. haenseleri
  tectorum L.   Narrow-leaved H.
  vesicaria L. subsp. haenseleri
    (DC.) P.D. Sell   Beaked H.

Crinitaria linosyris L. see Aster
  linosyris

Crithmum maritimum L.   Rock Samphire

Crocosmia x crocosmiflora
    (Lemoine) N.E. Br. see
    Tritonia x crocosmiflora

Crocus nudiflorus Sm.   Autumn Crocus
  purpureus Weston see C. vernus
    subsp. vernus
  sativus L.   Saffron C.
  vernus (L.) Hill subsp. vernus   Spring C.

Cruciata chersonensis auct. see
    Galium cruciata
  laevipes Opiz see Galium cruciata

Cryptogramma crispa (L.) Hooker   Parsley Fern

Cucubalus baccifer L.   Berry Catchfly

Cuscuta epilinum Weihe   Flax Dodder
  epithymum (L.) L.   Dodder
  europaea L.   Greater D.

Cyclamen hederifolium Aiton   Cyclamen
  neapolitanum Ten. see C.
    hederifolium

Cymbalaria muralis P. Gaertner,
    B. Meyer & Scherb.   Ivy-leaved Toadflax

Cynodon dactylon (L.) Pers.   Bermuda-grass

17

Cynoglossum germanicum

Cynoglossum germanicum Jacq.	Green Hound's-tongue
officinale L.	Hound's-tongue
Cynosurus cristatus L.	Crested Dog's-tail
echinatus L.	Rough D.
Cyperus fuscus L.	Brown Galingale
longus L.	Galingale
Cypripedium calceolus L.	Lady's-slipper
Cystopteris dickieana R. Sim	Dickie's Bladder-fern
fragilis (L.) Bernh.	Brittle B.
montana (Lam.) Desv.	Mountain B.
Cytisus scoparius (L.) Link	
subsp. maritimus (Rouy) Heywood	Prostrate Broom
subsp. scoparius	Broom
striatus (Hill.) Rothm.	Hairy-fruited B.

Daboecia cantabrica (Hudson) C. Koch	St Dabeoc's Heath
Dactylis glomerata L.	Cock's-foot
Dactylorchis see Dactylorhiza	
Dactylorhiza cruenta (O.F. Mueller) Soó	Flecked Marsh-orchid
fuchsii (Druce) Soó	Common Spotted-orchid
incarnata (L.) Soó	Early Marsh-orchid
kerryensis (Wilmott) P.F. Hunt &	
Summerhayes see D. majalis	
maculata L.	
subsp. ericetorum (Linton) P.F.	
Hunt & Summerhayes	Heath Spotted-orchid
majalis (Reichenb.) P.F. Hunt &	
Summerhayes	Broad-leaved Marsh-orchid
praetermissa (Druce) Soó	Southern M.
purpurella (T.& T.A. Steph.) Soó	Northern M.
traunsteineri (Sauter) Soó	Narrow-leaved M.
Damasonium alisma Miller	Starfruit
Danthonia decumbens (L.) DC.	Heath-grass
Daphne laureola L.	Spurge-laurel
mezereum L.	Mezereon
Datura stramonium L.	Thorn-apple
Daucus carota L.	
subsp. carota	Wild Carrot
subsp. gummifer Hooker fil.	Sea C.

Delphinium ambiguum L. see
    Consolida ambigua
ajacis auct. see Consolida ambigua
gayanum Wilmott see Consolida ambigua

Dentaria bulbifera L. see
    Cardamine bulbifera

Deschampsia alpina (L.) Roemer &
    Schultes   Alpine Hair-grass
cespitosa (L.) Beauv.   Tufted H.
flexuosa (L.) Trin.   Wavy H.
setacea (Hudson) Hackel   Bog H.

Descurainia sophia (L.) Prantl   Flixweed

Desmazeria marina (L.) Druce   Sea Fern-grass
rigida (L.) Tutin   Fern-grass

Dianthus armeria L.   Deptford Pink
barbatus L.   Sweet-William
caryophyllus L.   Clove Pink
deltoides L.   Maiden P.
gallicus L.   Jersey P.
gratianopolitanus Vill.   Cheddar P.
plumarius L.   Pink

Diapensia lapponica L.   Diapensia

Digitalis purpurea L.   Foxglove

Digitaria ischaemum (Schreber) Muhl.   Smooth Finger-grass
sanguinalis (L.) Scop.   Hairy F.

Diphasiastrum alpinum (L.) J. Holub   Alpine-clubmoss
x issleri (Rouy) J. Holub   Hybrid A.

Diphasium alpinum (L.) Rothm. see
    Diphasiastrum alpinum

Diplotaxis erucoides (L.) DC.   White Rocket
muralis (L.) DC.   Annual Wall-rocket
tenuifolia (L.) DC.   Perennial W.

Dipsacus fullonum L.
    subsp. fullonum   Fuller's Teasel
    subsp. sylvestris (Hudson) Clapham   Teasel
pilosus L.   Small T.
strigosus Roemer & Schultes   Yellow-flowered T.

Disphyma crassifolium (L.) L. Bolus   Purple Dew-plant

Doronicum pardalianches L.   Leopard's-bane
plantagineum L.   Plantain-leaved L.

Draba aizoides L.   Yellow Whitlowgrass

Draba - continued
  incana L.   Hoary Whitlowgrass
  muralis L.   Wall W.
  norvegica Gunnerus   Rock W.
  rupestris R. Br. see D. norvegica

Drosanthemum floribundum (Haw.)
  Schwant.   Pale Dew-plant

Drosera anglica Hudson   Great Sundew
  intermedia Hayne   Oblong-leaved S.
  rotundifolia L.   Round-leaved S.

Dryas octopetala L.   Mountain Avens

Dryopteris abbreviata (DC.) Newman
  see D. oreades
  aemula (Aiton) O. Kuntze   Hay-scented Buckler-fern
  affinis (Lowe) Fraser-Jenkins Scaly Male-fern
  assimilis S. Walker see D. expansa
  austriaca (Jacq.) Woynar see
    D. dilatata
  borreri Newman see D. affinis
  carthusiana (Vill.) H.P. Fuchs   Narrow Buckler-fern
  cristata (L.) A. Gray   Crested B.
  dilatata (Hoffm.) A. Gray   Broad B.
  expansa (C. Presl) Fraser-Jenkins
    & Jermy   Northern B.
  filix-mas (L.) Schott   Male-fern
  oreades Fomin   Mountain M.
  oreopteris (Ehrh.) Maxon see
    Oreopteris limbosperma
  pseudomas Wollaston see D. affinis
  spinulosa Watt see D. carthusiana
  villarii (Bellardi) Woyner ex
    Schinz & Thell.   Rigid Buckler-fern

Duchesnea indica (Andr.) Focke   Yellow-flowered
                                Strawberry

Echinochloa crus-galli (L.) Beauv.   Cockspur

Echium lycopsis L. see E. plantagineum
  plantagineum L.   Purple Viper's-bugloss
  vulgare L.   Viper's-bugloss

Egeria densa Planchon   Large-flowered Waterweed

Elatine hexandra (Lapierre) DC.   Six-stamened Waterwort
  hydropiper L.   Eight-stamened W.

Eleocharis acicularis (L.) Roemer
    & Schultes   Needle Spike-rush
  austriaca Hayek   Northern S.

Eleocharis - continued
  multicaulis (Sm.) Desv.   Many-stalked Spike-rush
  palustris (L.) Roemer & Schultes   Common S.
  parvula (Roemer & Schultes) Bluff,
    Nees & Schauer   Dwarf S.
  quinqueflora (F.X. Hartmann) O.
    Schwarz   Few-flowered S.
  uniglumis (Link) Schultes   Slender S.

Eleogiton fluitans (L.) Link   Floating Club-rush

Elodea callitrichoides (Rich.) Casp. South American Waterweed
  canadensis Michx   Canadian W.
  ernstiae St John see E.
    callitrichoides
  nuttallii (Planchon) St John   Nuttall's W.

Elymus arenarius L. see Leymus arenarius
  caninus (L.) L. (including
    Agropyron donianum F.B. White) Bearded Couch
  farctus (Viv.) Melderis   Sand C.
  pycnanthus (Godron) Melderis   Sea C.
  repens (L.) Gould   Common C.

Empetrum hermaphroditum Hagerup
    see E. nigrum subsp. hermaphroditum
  nigrum L.
    subsp. nigrum   Crowberry
    subsp. hermaphroditum (Hagerup)
      Bocher   Mountain C.

Endymion hispanicus (Miller)
    Chouard see Hyacinthoides
    hispanica
  non-scriptus (L.) Garcke see
    Hyacinthoides non-scripta

Epilobium adenocaulon Hausskn.
    see E. ciliatum
  alsinifolium Vill.   Chickweed Willowherb
  anagallidifolium Lam.   Alpine W.
  angustifolium L. see Chamerion
    angustifolium
  brunnescens (Cockayne) Raven &
    Engelhorn   New Zealand W.
  ciliatum Rafin.   American W.
  hirsutum L.   Great W.
  lanceolatum Sebastiani & Mauri   Spear-leaved W.
  montanum L.   Broad-leaved W.
  nerterioides auct. see E. brunnescens
  obscurum Schreber   Short-fruited W.
  palustre L.   Marsh W.
  parviflorum Schreber   Hoary W.
  roseum Schreber   Pale W.
  tetragonum L.   Square-stalked W.

Epipactis atrorubens

Epipactis atrorubens (Hoffm.) Besser	Dark-red Helleborine
dunensis (T. & T.A. Stephenson) Godf.	Dune H.
helleborine (L.) Crantz	Broad-leaved H.
leptochila (Godf.) Godf.	Narrow-lipped H.
palustris (L.) Crantz	Marsh H.
phyllanthes G.E. Sm.	Green-flowered H.
purpurata Sm.	Violet H.
Epipogium aphyllum Swartz	Ghost Orchid
Equisetum arvense L.	Field Horsetail
fluviatile L.	Water H.
hyemale L.	Rough H.
palustre L.	Marsh H.
pratense Ehrh.	Shady H.
sylvaticum L.	Wood H.
telmateia Ehrh.	Great H.
variegatum Weber & Mohr	Variegated H.
Eranthis hyemalis (L.) Salisb.	Winter Aconite
Erica ciliaris L.	Dorset Heath
cinerea L.	Bell Heather
erigena R. Ross	Irish Heath
mackaiana Bab.	Mackay's H.
mediterranea L. see E. erigena	
terminalis Salisb.	Corsican H.
tetralix L.	Cross-leaved H.
vagans L.	Cornish H.
Erigeron acer L.	Blue Fleabane
bonariensis L.	Argentine F.
borealis (Vierh.) Simmons	Alpine F.
canadensis L.	Canadian F.
mucronatus DC.	Mexican F.
Erinus alpinus L.	Fairy Foxglove
Eriocaulon aquaticum (Hill) Druce	Pipewort
septangulare With. see E. aquaticum	
Eriophorum angustifolium Honckeny	Common Cottongrass
gracile Roth	Slender C.
latifolium Hoppe	Broad-leaved C.
vaginatum L.	Hare's-tail C.
Erodium cicutarium (L.) L'Hér.	
subsp. bipinnatum (Willd.) Tourlet	Sticky Stork's-bill
subsp. cicutarium	Common S.
glutinosum Dumort. see E.	
cicutarium subsp. bipinnatum	
maritimum (L.) L'Hér.	Sea S.
moschatum (L.) L'Hér.	Musk S.
Erophila spathulata Lang	Round-podded Whitlowgrass
verna (L.) Chevall.	Common W.

Eruca vesicaria (L.) Cav. subsp. sativa (Miller) Thell.	Garden Rocket
Erucastrum gallicum (Willd.) O.E. Schulz	Hairy R.
Eryngium campestre L. maritimum L.	Field Eryngo Sea-holly
Erysimum cheiranthoides L.	Treacle Mustard
Escallonia macrantha Hooker & Arnott	Escallonia
Eschscholzia californica Cham.	Californian Poppy
Euonymus europaeus L.	Spindle
Eupatorium cannabinum L.	Hemp-agrimony

Euphorbia amygdaloides L.
  corallioides L.
  cyparissias L.
  dulcis L.
  esula L.
  exigua L.
  helioscopia L.
  hyberna L.
  lathyrus L.
  paralias L.
  peplis L.
  peplus L.
  platyphyllos L.
  portlandica L.
  serrulata Thuill.
  uralensis auct. see E. esula
  villosa Willd.
	Wood Spurge
	Coral S.
	Cypress S.
	Sweet S.
	Leafy S.
	Dwarf S.
	Sun S.
	Irish S.
	Caper S.
	Sea S.
	Purple S.
	Petty S.
	Broad-leaved S.
	Portland S.
	Upright S.
	
	Hairy S.

Euphrasia officinalis L. salisburgensis Funck	Eyebright Irish E.
Exaculum pusillum (Lam.) Caruel	Guernsey Centaury
Fagopyrum esculentum Moench tataricum (L.) Gaertner	Buckwheat Green B.
Fagus sylvatica L.	Beech
Falcaria vulgaris Bernh.	Longleaf

Fallopia aubertii (Louis Henry) J. Holub
  baldschuanica (Regel) J. Holub
    see F. aubertii
  convolvulus (L.) A. Löve
  dumetorum (L.) J. Holub
	Russian-vine
	
	Black-bindweed
	Copse-bindweed

23

Festuca altissima

Festuca altissima All.	Wood Fescue
armoricana Kerguélen	Breton F.
arundinacea Schreber	Tall F.
caesia Sm. see F. longifolia	
fallax Thuill. see F. nigrescens	
gigantea (L.) Vill.	Giant F.
glauca auct. see F. longifolia	
heterophylla Lam.	Various-leaved F.
juncifolia St-Amans	Rush-leaved F.
longifolia auct., non Thuill. see F. trachyphylla	
longifolia Thuill.	Blue F.
nigrescens Lam.	Chewings F.
ovina L.	Sheep's-fescue
pratensis Hudson	Meadow Fescue
rubra L.	Red F.
rubra L. subsp. commutata Gaudin see F. nigrescens	
tenuifolia Sibth.	Fine-leaved Sheep's-fescue
trachyphylla (Hackel) Krajina	Hard Fescue
vivipara (L.) Sm.	Viviparous F.
x Festulolium loliaceum (Hudson) P. Fourn.	Hybrid F.
Ficus carica L.	Fig
Filago apiculata G.E. Sm. ex Bab. see F. lutescens	
gallica L.	Narrow-leaved Cudweed
germanica L., non Hudson see F. vulgaris	
lutescens Jordan	Red-tipped C.
minima (Sm.) Pers.	Small C.
pyramidata L.	Broad-leaved C.
spathulata C. Presl see F. pyramidata	
vulgaris Lam.	Common C.
Filipendula ulmaria (L.) Maxim.	Meadowsweet
vulgaris Moench	Dropwort
Foeniculum vulgare Miller	Fennel
Fragaria x ananassa Duchesne	Garden Strawberry
moschata Duchesne	Hautbois S.
vesca L.	Wild S.
Frangula alnus Miller	Alder Buckthorn
Frankenia laevis L.	Sea-heath
Fraxinus excelsior L.	Ash
Fritillaria meleagris L.	Fritillary
Fuchsia magellanica Lam.	Fuchsia

24

Fumaria bastardii Boreau
  capreolata L.
  densiflora DC.
  martinii Clavaud
  micrantha Lag. see F. densiflora
  muralis Koch
  occidentalis Pugsley
  officinalis L.
  parviflora Lam.
  purpurea Pugsley
  vaillantii Loisel.

Tall Ramping-fumitory
White R.
Dense-flowered Fumitory
Martin's Ramping-fumitory

Common R.
Western R.
Common Fumitory
Fine-leaved F.
Purple Ramping-fumitory
Few-flowered Fumitory

Gagea bohemica (Zauschner) Schultes
    & Schultes fil.
  lutea (L.) Ker-Gawler

Early Star-of-Bethlehem
Yellow S.

Galanthus nivalis L.

Snowdrop

Galega officinalis L.

Goat's-rue

Galeobdolon luteum Hudson see
    Lamiastrum galeobdolon

Galeopsis angustifolia Hoffm.
  bifida Boenn.
  ladanum L.
  segetum Necker
  speciosa Miller
  tetrahit L.

Red Hemp-nettle
Lesser H.
Broad-leaved H.
Downy H.
Large-flowered H.
Common H.

Galinsoga ciliata (Rafin.) S.F. Blake
  parviflora Cav.

Shaggy Soldier
Gallant S.

Galium album Miller
  aparine L.
  boreale L.
  cruciata (L.) Scop.
  debile Desv.
  elongatum C. Presl
  erectum Hudson see G. album
  fleurotii Jordan
  mollugo L.
  odoratum (L.) Scop.
  palustre L.
  parisiense L.
  pumilum Murray
  saxatile L.
  spurium L.
  sterneri Ehrend.
  tricornutum Dandy
  uliginosum L.
  verum L.

Upright Hedge-bedstraw
Cleavers
Northern Bedstraw
Crosswort
Slender Marsh-bedstraw
Great M.

Cheddar Bedstraw
Hedge-bedstraw
Woodruff
Common Marsh-bedstraw
Wall Bedstraw
Slender B.
Heath B.
False Cleavers
Limestone Bedstraw
Corn Cleavers
Fen Bedstraw
Lady's B.

Gastridium <u>ventricosum</u>

Gastridium ventricosum (Gouan) Schinz & Thell.	Nit-grass
Gaultheria shallon Pursh	Shallon
Genista anglica L.	Petty Whin
pilosa L.	Hairy Greenweed
tinctoria L.	Dyer's G.
Gentiana nivalis L.	Alpine Gentian
pneumonanthe L.	Marsh G.
verna L.	Spring G.
Gentianella amarella (L.) Borner	Autumn G.
anglica (Pugsley) E.F. Warburg	Early G.
campestris (L.) Borner	Field G.
germanica (Willd.) Borner	Chiltern G.
uliginosa (Willd.) Borner	Dune G.
Geranium columbinum L.	Long-stalked Crane's-bill
dissectum L.	Cut-leaved C.
endressii Gay	French C.
lucidum L.	Shining C.
molle L.	Dove's-foot C.
nodosum L.	Knotted C.
phaeum L.	Dusky C.
pratense L.	Meadow C.
purpureum Vill.	Little-Robin
pusillum L.	Small-flowered Crane's-bill
pyrenaicum Burm. fil.	Hedgerow C.
robertianum L.	Herb-Robert
rotundifolium L.	Round-leaved Crane's-bill
sanguineum L.	Bloody C.
sylvaticum L.	Wood C.
versicolor L.	Pencilled C.
Geum x intermedium Ehrh.	Hybrid Avens
rivale L.	Water A.
urbanum L.	Wood A.
Gladiolus illyricus Koch	Wild Gladiolus
Glaucium flavum Crantz	Yellow Horned-poppy
Glaux maritima L.	Sea-milkwort
Glechoma hederacea L.	Ground-ivy
Glyceria declinata Bréb.	Small Sweet-grass
fluitans (L.) R. Br.	Floating S.
maxima (Hartman) Holmberg	Reed S.
x pedicellata Townsend	Hybrid S.
plicata Fries	Plicate S.
Gnaphalium luteo-album L.	Jersey Cudweed
norvegicum Gunnerus	Highland C.

26

Gnaphalium - continued
  supinum L.   Dwarf Cudweed
  sylvaticum L.   Heath C.
  uliginosum L.   Marsh C.

Goodyera repens (L.) R. Br.   Creeping Lady's-tresses

Groenlandia densa (L.) Fourr.   Opposite-leaved Pondweed

Gunnera manicata André   Brazilian Giant-rhubarb
  tinctoria (Molina) Mirbel   Giant-rhubarb

Gymnadenia conopsea (L.) R. Br.   Fragrant Orchid

Gymnocarpium dryopteris (L.) Newman Oak' Fern
  robertianum (Hoffm.) Newman   Limestone F.

Halimione portulacoides (L.) Aellen Sea-purslane

Hammarbya paludosa (L.) O. Kuntze   Bog Orchid

Hebe x franciscana (Eastw.) Souster Hedge Veronica
  salicifolia (G. Forster) Pennell Koromiko

Hedera helix L.   Ivy
  hibernica (DC.) Bean   Irish I.

Helianthemum apenninum (L.) Miller   White Rock-rose
  canum (L.) Baumg.   Hoary R.
  chamaecistus Miller see H. nummularium
  nummularium (L.) Miller   Common R.

Helianthus annuus L.   Sunflower

Helictotrichon pratense (L.)
  Besser see Avenula pratensis
  pubescens (Hudson) Besser see
    Avenula pubescens

Helleborus foetidus L.   Stinking Hellebore
  viridis L.   Green H.

Helxine soleirolii Req. see
  Soleirolia soleirolii

Heracleum mantegazzianum Sommier &
  Levier   Giant Hogweed
  sphondylium L.   Hogweed

Herminium monorchis (L.) R. Br.   Musk Orchid

Hermodactylus tuberosus (L.) Miller Snake's-head Iris

Herniaria ciliolata

Herniaria ciliolata Melderis	Fringed Rupturewort
glabra L.	Smooth R.
hirsuta L.	Hairy R.
Hesperis matronalis L.	Dame's-violet
Hieracium aurantiacum L.	Fox-and-cubs
maculatum Sm.	Spotted Hawkweed
pilosella L.	Mouse-ear H.
vulgatum Fries	Common H.
Hierochloe odorata (L.) Beauv.	Holy-grass
Himantoglossum hircinum (L.) Sprengel	Lizard Orchid
Hippocrepis comosa L.	Horseshoe Vetch
Hippophae rhamnoides L.	Sea-buckthorn
Hippuris vulgaris L.	Mare's-tail
Hirschfeldia incana (L.) Lagrèze-Fossat	Hoary Mustard
Holcus lanatus L.	Yorkshire-fog
mollis L.	Creeping Soft-grass
Holoschoenus vulgaris Link	Round-headed Club-rush
Homogyne alpina (L.) Cass.	Purple Colt's-foot
Honkenya peploides (L.) Ehrh.	Sea Sandwort
Hordelymus europaeus (L.) Harz	Wood Barley
Hordeum jubatum L.	Foxtail B.
marinum Hudson	Sea B.
murinum L.	Wall B.
secalinum Schreber	Meadow B.
Hornungia petraea (L.) Reichenb.	Hutchinsia
Hottonia palustris L.	Water-violet
Humulus lupulus L.	Hop
Huperzia selago (L.) Schrank & Mart.	Fir Clubmoss
Hyacinthoides hispanica (Miller) Rothm.	Spanish Bluebell
non-scripta (L.) Rothm.	Bluebell
Hydrilla verticillata (L. fil.) Royle	Hydrilla
Hydrocharis morsus-ranae L.	Frogbit
Hydrocotyle moschata G. Forster	Hairy Pennywort
vulgaris L.	Marsh P.

Hymenophyllum tunbrigense (L.) Sm.   Tonbridge Filmy-fern
  wilsonii Hooker   Wilson's F.

Hyoscyamus niger L.   •   Henbane

Hypericum androsaemum L.   Tutsan
  calycinum L.   Rose-of-Sharon
  canadense L.   Irish St John's-wort
  elodes L.   Marsh S.
  hircinum L.   Stinking Tutsan
  hirsutum L.   Hairy St John's-wort
  humifusum L.   Trailing S.
  inodorum Miller   Tall Tutsan
  linarifolium Vahl   Toadflax-leaved
                                        St John's-wort
  maculatum Crantz   Imperforate S.
  montanum L.   Pale S.
  perforatum L.   Perforate S.
  pulchrum L.   Slender S.
  tetrapterum Fries   Square-stalked S.
  undulatum Willd.   Wavy S.

Hypochoeris glabra L.   Smooth Cat's-ear
  maculata L.   Spotted C.
  radicata L.   Cat's-ear

Hyssopus officinalis L.   Hyssop

Iberis amara L.   Wild Candytuft
  umbellata L.   Garden C.

Ilex aquifolium L.   Holly

Illecebrum verticillatum L.   Coral-necklace

Impatiens capensis Meerb.   Orange Balsam
  glandulifera Royle   Indian B.
  noli-tangere L.   Touch-me-not B.
  parviflora DC.   Small B.

Inula conyza DC.   Ploughman's-spikenard
  crithmoides L.   Golden-samphire
  helenium L.   Elecampane
  salicina L.   Irish Fleabane

Iris foetidissima L.   Stinking Iris
  germanica L.   Flag I.
  pseudacorus L.   Yellow I.
  spuria L.   Blue I.
  versicolor L.   Purple I.

Isatis tinctoria L.   Woad

<u>Isoetes echinospora</u>

Isoetes echinospora Durieu	Spring Quillwort
histrix Bory	Land Quillwort
lacustris L.	Quillwort
setacea auct. <u>see</u> I. echinospora	
Isolepis cernua (Vahl) Roemer & Schultes	Slender Club-rush
setacea (L.) R. Br.	Bristle C.

Jasione montana L.	Sheep's-bit
Juglans regia L.	Walnut
Juncus acutiflorus Hoffm.	Sharp-flowered Rush
acutus L.	Sharp R.
alpinoarticulatus auct., non Chaix <u>see</u> J. alpinus	
alpinus Vill.	Alpine R.
articulatus L.	Jointed R.
balticus Willd.	Baltic R.
biglumis L.	Two-flowered R.
bufonius L.	Toad R.
bulbosus L.	Bulbous R.
capitatus Weigel	Dwarf R.
castaneus Sm.	Chestnut R.
compressus Jacq.	Round-fruited R.
conglomeratus L.	Compact R.
x diffusus Hoppe	Diffuse R.
dudleyi Wiegand	Dudley's R.
effusus L.	Soft-rush
filiformis L.	Thread Rush
foliosus Desf. <u>see</u> J. bufonius	
gerardi Loisel.	Saltmarsh R.
inflexus L.	Hard R.
kochii Schultz <u>see</u> J. bulbosus	
maritimus Lam.	Sea R.
mutabilis Lam. <u>see</u> J. pygmaeus	
nodulosus Wahlenb.	Marshall's R.
pallidus R. Br.	Great Soft-rush
planifolius R. Br.	Broad-leaved Rush
pygmaeus L.C.M. Richard	Pigmy R.
squarrosus L.	Heath R.
subnodulosus Schrank	Blunt-flowered R.
subuliflorus Drejer <u>see</u> J. conglomeratus	
tenuis Willd.	Slender R.
trifidus L.	Three-leaved R.
triglumis L.	Three-flowered R.
Juniperus communis L.	Juniper

Kickxia elatine (L.) Dumort.	Sharp-leaved Fluellen
spuria (L.) Dumort.	Round-leaved F.
Knautia arvensis (L.) Coulter	Field Scabious
Kobresia simpliciuscula (Wahlenb.) Mackenzie	False Sedge
Koeleria cristata (L.) Pers. pro parte see K. macrantha	
glauca (Schrader) DC.	Dune Hair-grass
macrantha (Ledeb.) Schultes	Crested H.
vallesiana (Honckeny) Gaudin	Somerset H.
Koenigia islandica L.	Iceland-purslane

Laburnum anagyroides Medicus	Laburnum
Lactuca saligna L.	Least Lettuce
sativa L.	Garden L.
serriola L.	Prickly L.
virosa L.	Great L.
Lagarosiphon major (Ridley) Moss	Curly Waterweed
Lagurus ovatus L.	Hare's-tail
Lamiastrum galeobdolon (L.) Ehrend. & Polatschek	Yellow Archangel
Lamium album L.	White Dead-nettle
amplexicaule L.	Henbit D.
hybridum Vill.	Cut-leaved D.
maculatum L.	Spotted D.
moluccellifolium Fries	Northern D.
purpureum L.	Red D.
Lampranthus deltoides (Miller) Glen	Deltoid-leaved Dew-plant
falciformis (Haw.) N.E. Br.	Sickle-leaved D.
roseus (Willd.) Schwantes	Rosy D.
Lapsana communis L.	Nipplewort
Larix decidua Miller	European Larch
kaempferi (Lamb.) Carrière	Japanese L.
leptolepis (Siebold & Zucc.) Endl. see L. kaempferi	
Lathraea clandestina L.	Purple Toothwort
squamaria L.	Toothwort
Lathyrus aphaca L.	Yellow Vetchling
hirsutus L.	Hairy V.

Lathyrus - continued
    japonicus Willd.   Sea Pea
    latifolius L.   Broad-leaved
                                            Everlasting-pea
    montanus Bernh.   Bitter-vetch
    niger (L.) Bernh.   Black Pea
    nissolia L.   Grass Vetchling
    palustris L.   Marsh Pea
    pratensis L.   Meadow Vetchling
    sylvestris L.   Narrow-leaved
                                            Everlasting-pea
    tuberosus L.   Tuberous Pea

Lavatera arborea L.   Tree-mallow
    cretica L.   Smaller T.

Ledum groenlandicum Oed. see L.
      palustre
    palustre L.   Labrador-tea

Leersia oryzoides (L.) Swartz   Cut-grass

Legousia hybrida (L.) Delarbre   Venus's-looking-glass

Lemna gibba L.   Fat Duckweed
    minor L.   Common D.
    minuscula L.   Least D.
    polyrhiza L.   Greater D.
    trisulca L.   Ivy-leaved D.

Leontodon autumnalis L.   Autumn Hawkbit
    hispidus L.   Rough H.
    taraxacoides (Vill.) Mérat   Lesser H.

Leonurus cardiaca L.   Motherwort

Lepidium campestre (L.) R. Br.   Field Pepperwort
    graminifolium L.   Tall P.
    heterophyllum Bentham   Smith's P.
    latifolium L.   Dittander
    neglectum Thell.   Least Pepperwort
    ruderale L.   Narrow-leaved P.
    sativum L.   Garden Cress

Leucanthemum maximum (Ramond) DC.   Shasta Daisy
    vulgare Lam.   Oxeye D.

Leucojum aestivum L.   Summer Snowflake
    vernum L.   Spring S.

Leucorchis albida (L.) Schur see
      Pseudorchis albida (L.) Á. &
      D. Löve

Leycesteria formosa Wall.   Himalayan Honeysuckle

Leymus arenarius (L.) Hochst.   Lyme-grass

Ligusticum scoticum L.   Scots Lovage

Ligustrum ovalifolium Hassk.   Garden Privet
  vulgare L.   Wild P.

Lilium martagon L.   Martagon Lily
  pyrenaicum L.   Pyrenean L.

Limonium auriculae-ursifolium
    (Pourret) Druce   Jersey Sea-lavender
  auriculae-ursifolium auct., non
    (Pourret) Druce see L.
    normannicum
  bellidifolium (Gouan) Dumort.   Matted S.
  binervosum (G.E. Sm.) C.E. Salmon   Rock S.
  humile Miller   Lax-flowered S.
  normannicum Ingrouille   Alderney S.
  vulgare Miller   Common S.

Limosella aquatica L.   Mudwort
  australis R. Br.   Welsh M.
  subulata Ives see L. australis

Linaria arenaria DC.   Sand Toadflax
  pelisseriana (L.) Miller   Jersey T.
  purpurea (L.) Miller   Purple T.
  repens (L.) Miller   Pale T.
  supina (L.) Chaz.   Prostrate T.
  vulgaris Miller   Common T.

Linnaea borealis L.   Twinflower

Linum anglicum Miller see L.
    perenne subsp. anglicum
  bienne Miller   Pale Flax
  catharticum L.   Fairy F.
  perenne L. subsp. anglicum
    (Miller) Ockendon   Perennial F.
  usitatissimum L.   Flax

Liparis loeselii (L.) L.C.M. Richard   Fen Orchid

Listera cordata (L.) R. Br.   Lesser Twayblade
  ovata (L.) R. Br.   Common T.

Lithospermum arvense L.   Field Gromwell
  officinale L.   Common G.
  purpurocaeruleum L.   Purple G.

Littorella uniflora (L.) Ascherson   Shoreweed

Lloydia serotina (L.) Reichenb.   Snowdon Lily

Lobelia dortmanna L.   Water Lobelia
  urens L.   Heath L.

Lobularia maritima

Lobularia maritima (L.) Desv.	Sweet Alison

Logfia gallica (L.) Cosson & Germ.
   see Filago gallica
   minima (L.) Dumort. see Filago
   minima

Loiseleuria procumbens (L.) Desv.	Trailing Azalea

Lolium multiflorum Lam. see L.
   perenne subsp. multiflorum
perenne L.

subsp. multiflorum (Lam.) Husnot	Italian Rye-grass
subsp. perenne	Perennial R.
temulentum L.	Darnel
Lonicera caprifolium L.	Perfoliate Honeysuckle
periclymenum L.	Honeysuckle
xylosteum L.	Fly H.
Lotus angustissimus L.	Slender Bird's-foot- trefoil
corniculatus L.	Common B.
hispidus DC. see L. subbiflorus	
pedunculatus Cav. see L. uliginosus	
subbiflorus Lag.	Hairy B.
tenuis Willd.	Narrow-leaved B.
uliginosus Schkuhr	Greater B.
Ludwigia palustris (L.) Elliott	Hampshire-purslane
Lunaria annua L.	Honesty
Lupinus arboreus Sims	Tree Lupin
nootkatensis Sims	Nootka L.
polyphyllus Lindley	Garden L.
Luronium natans (L.) Rafin	Floating Water-plantain
Luzula arcuata Sw.	Curved Wood-rush
campestris (L.) DC.	Field W.
forsteri (Sm.) DC.	Southern W.
luzuloides (Lam.) Dandy & Wilmott	White W.
multiflora (Retz.) Lej.	Heath W.
nivea (L.) DC.	Snow-white W.
pallescens Swartz	Fen W.
pilosa (L.) Willd.	Hairy W.
spicata (L.) DC.	Spiked W.
sylvatica (Hudson) Gaudin	Great W.
Lychnis alpina L.	Alpine Catchfly
flos-cuculi L.	Ragged-Robin
viscaria L.	Sticky Catchfly
Lycium barbarum L.	Duke of Argyll's Teaplant
chinense Miller	China T.
halimifolium Miller see L. barbarum	

Lycopodiella inundata (L.) J. Holub   Marsh Clubmoss

Lycopodium alpinum L. see
   Diphasiastrum alpinum
  annotinum L.   Interrupted C.
  clavatum L.   Stag's-horn C.
  inundatum L. see Lycopodiella
   inundatum
  issleri (Rouy) Lawalrée see
   Diphasiastrum issleri
  selago L. see Huperzia selago

Lycopsis arvensis L. see Anchusa
  arvensis

Lycopus europaeus L.   Gipsywort

Lysimachia ciliata L.   Fringed Loosestrife
  nemorum L.   Yellow Pimpernel
  nummularia L.   Creeping-Jenny
  punctata L.   Dotted Loosestrife
  terrestris (L.) Britton, E.E.
   Sterns & Poggenb.   Lake L.
  thyrsiflora L.   Tufted L.
  vulgaris L.   Yellow L.

Lythrum hyssopifolia L.   Grass-poly
  portula (L.) D.A. Webb   Water-purslane
  salicaria L.   Purple-loosestrife

Mahonia aquifolium (Pursh) Nutt.   Oregon-grape

Maianthemum bifolium (L.) F.W. Schmidt   May Lily

Malus sylvestris Miller   Crab Apple

Malva moschata L.   Musk Mallow
  neglecta Wallr.   Dwarf M.
  parviflora L.   Least M.
  pusilla Sm.   Small M.
  sylvestris L.   Common M.
  verticillata L.   Chinese M.

Marrubium vulgare L.   White Horehound

Matricaria chamomilla L. pro parte
  see M. recutita
  maritima L. see Tripleurospermum
   maritimum
  matricarioides (Less.) Porter   Pineappleweed
  recutita L.   Scented Mayweed

Matteuccia struthiopteris (L.) Tod.   Ostrich Fern

Matthiola incana

Matthiola incana (L.) R. Br.	Hoary Stock
sinuata (L.) R. Br.	Sea S.
Meconopsis cambrica (L.) Vig.	Welsh Poppy
Medicago arabica (L.) Hudson	Spotted Medick
falcata L.	Sickle M.
lupulina L.	Black M.
minima (L.) L.	Bur M.
polymorpha L.	Toothed M.
' sativa L.	Lucerne
Melampyrum arvense L.	Field Cow-wheat
cristatum L.	Crested C.
pratense L.	Common C.
sylvaticum L.	Small C.
Melica nutans L.	Mountain Melick
uniflora Retz.	Wood M.
Melilotus alba Medicus	White Melilot
altissima Thuill.	Tall M.
indica (L.) All.	Small M.
officinalis (L.) Pallas	Ribbed M.
Melissa officinalis L.	Balm
Melittis melissophyllum L.	Bastard B.
Mentha aquatica L.	Water Mint
arvensis L.	Corn M.
x gentilis L.	Bushy M.
longifolia auctt. non (L.) Hudson see	
M. spicata	
x piperita L.	Peppermint
pulegium L.	Pennyroyal
requienii Bentham	Corsican Mint
rotundifolia auct., non (L.)	
Hudson see M. suaveolens	
spicata L.	Spear M.
suaveolens Ehrh.	Round-leaved M.
x verticillata L.	Whorled M.
x villosa Hudson	Apple M.
Menyanthes trifoliata L.	Bogbean
Mercurialis annua L.	Annual Mercury
perennis L.	Dog's M.
Mertensia maritima (L.) S.F. Gray	Oysterplant
Mespilus germanica L.	Medlar
Meum athamanticum Jacq.	Spignel
Mibora minima (L.) Desv.	Early Sand-grass

Milium effusum L.   Wood Millet
   scabrum L.C.M. Richard see M. vernale
   vernale Bieb.   Early M.

Mimulus guttatus DC.   Monkeyflower
   luteus L.   Blood-drop-emlets
   moschatus Lindley   Musk

Minuartia hybrida (Vill.) Schischkin   Fine-leaved Sandwort
   recurva (All.) Schinz & Thell.   Recurved S.
   rubella (Wahlenb.) Hiern   Mountain S.
   sedoides (L.) Hiern   Cyphel
   stricta (Swartz) Hiern   Teesdale Sandwort
   verna (L.) Hiern   Spring S.

Misopates orontium (L.) Rafin.   Lesser Snapdragon

Moehringia trinervia (L.) Clairv.   Three-nerved Sandwort

Moenchia erecta (L.) P. Gaertner,
   B. Meyer & Scherb.   Upright Chickweed

Molinia caerulea (L.) Moench   Purple Moor-grass

Moneses uniflora (L.) A. Gray   One-flowered Wintergreen

Monotropa hypophegea Wallr. see
   M. hypopitys
   hypopitys L.   Yellow Bird's-nest

Montia fontana L.   Blinks
   perfoliata (Willd.) Howell   Springbeauty
   sibirica (L.) Howell   Pink Purslane

Muehlenbeckia complexa (A. Cunn.)
   Meissner   Wireplant

Muscari atlanticum Boiss. & Reuter
   see M. neglectum
   neglectum Ten.   Grape Hyacinth
   racemosum auct. see M. neglectum

Mycelis muralis (L.) Dumort.   Wall Lettuce

Myosotis alpestris F.W. Schmidt   Alpine Forget-me-not
   arvensis (L.) Hill   Field F.
   brevifolia C.E. Salmon see M.
      stolonifera
   caespitosa C.F. Schultz see M.
      laxa subsp. caespitosa
   discolor Pers.   Changing F.
   hispida Schlecht. see M. ramosissima
   laxa Lehm. subsp. caespitosa
      (C.F. Schultz) Hylander   Tufted F.
   ramosissima Rochel   Early F.
   scorpioides L.   Water F.

37

Myosotis secunda

Myosotis - continued
  secunda A. Murray   Creeping Forget-me-not
  sicula Guss.   Jersey F.
  stolonifera (DC.) Leresche & Levier   Pale F.
  sylvatica Hoffm.   Wood F.

Myosoton aquaticum (L.) Moench   Water Chickweed

Myosurus minimus L.   Mousetail

Myrica gale L.   Bog-myrtle

Myriophyllum alterniflorum DC.   Alternate Water-milfoil
  spicatum L.   Spiked W.
  verticillatum L.   Whorled W.

Myrrhis odorata (L.) Scop.   Sweet Cicely

Najas flexilis (Willd.) Rostk. &
    W.L.E. Schmidt   Slender Naiad
  marina L.   Holly-leaved N.

Narcissus x biflorus Curtis see
    N. x medioluteus
  hispanicus Gouan   Spanish Daffodil
  jonquilla L.   Jonquil
x medioluteus Miller   Primrose-peerless
  obvallaris Salisb.   Tenby Daffodil
  poeticus L.   Pheasant's-eye D.
  pseudonarcissus L.   Wild D.
  tazetta L.   Bunch-flowered D.

Nardurus maritimus (L.) Murb. see
    Vulpia unilateralis

Nardus stricta L.   Mat-grass

Narthecium ossifragum (L.) Hudson   Bog Asphodel

Nasturtium microphyllum (Boenn.)
    Reichenb.   Narrow-fruited Water-cress
  officinale R. Br.   Water-cress
x sterile (Airy Shaw) Oefelein   Hybrid W.

Neotinea intacta (Link) Reichenb.
    fil. see N. maculata
  maculata (Desf.) Stearn   Dense-flowered Orchid

Neottia nidus-avis (L.) L.C.M. Richard   Bird's-nest O.

Nepeta cataria L.   Cat-mint

Neslia paniculata (L.) Desv.   Ball Mustard

Nicandra physalodes (L.) Gaertner   Apple-of-Peru

Nuphar lutea (L.) Sm.   Yellow Water-lily
x intermedia Ledeb.   Hybrid W.
  pumila (Timm) DC.   Least W.

Nymphaea alba L.   White W.

Nymphoides peltata (S.G. Gmelin)
  O. Kuntze   Fringed W.

Odontites verna (Bellardi) Dumort.   Red Bartsia

Oenanthe aquatica (L.) Poiret   Fine-leaved Water-dropwort
  crocata L.   Hemlock W.
  fistulosa L.   Tubular W.
  fluviatilis (Bab.) Coleman   River W.
  lachenalii C.C. Gmelin   Parsley W.
  pimpinelloides L.   Corky-fruited W.
  silaifolia Bieb.   Narrow-leaved W.

Oenothera biennis L.   Common Evening-primrose
  cambrica Rost.   Small-flowered E.
  erythrosepala Borbás   Large-flowered E.
  lamarckiana de Vries, non Ser.
    see O. erythrosepala
  odorata Jacq. pro parte see O.
    stricta
  parviflora auct. see O. cambrica
  stricta Link.   Fragrant E.

Omphalodes verna Moench   Blue-eyed-Mary

Onobrychis viciifolia Scop.   Sainfoin

Onoclea sensibilis L.   Sensitive Fern

Ononis reclinata L.   Small Restharrow
  repens L.   Common R.
  spinosa L.   Spiny R.

Onopordum acanthium L.   Cotton Thistle

Ophioglossum azoricum C. Presl   Small Adder's-tongue
  lusitanicum L.   Least A.
  vulgatum L.   Adder's-tongue

Ophrys apifera Hudson   Bee Orchid
  fuciflora (Crantz) Moench   Late Spider-orchid
  insectifera L.   Fly Orchid
  sphegodes Miller   Early Spider-Orchid

<u>Orchis</u> <u>laxiflora</u>

Orchis laxiflora Lam.   Loose-flowered Orchid
  mascula (L.) L.   Early-purple O.
  militaris L.   Military O.
  morio L.   Green-winged O.
  purpurea Hudson   Lady O.
  simia Lam.   Monkey O.
  ustulata L.   Burnt O.

Oreopteris limbosperma (All.) J. Holub   Lemon-scented Fern

Origanum vulgare L.   Marjoram

Ornithogalum nutans L.   Drooping Star-of-Bethlehem
  pyrenaicum L.   Spiked S.
  umbellatum L.   Star-of-Bethlehem

Ornithopus perpusillus L.   Bird's-foot
  pinnatus (Miller) Druce   Orange B.

Orobanche alba Willd.   Thyme Broomrape
  caryophyllacea Sm.   Bedstraw B.
  elatior Sutton   Knapweed B.
  hederae Duby   Ivy B.
  loricata Reichenb.   Oxtongue B.
  maritima Pugsley   Carrot B.
  minor Sm.   Common B.
  picridis Koch <u>see</u> O. loricata
  purpurea Jacq.   Yarrow B.
  ramosa L.   Hemp B.
  rapum-genistae Thuill.   Greater B.
  reticulata Wallr.   Thistle B.

Orthilia secunda (L.) House   Serrated Wintergreen

Oscularia deltoides (Miller) Schwantes
    <u>see</u> Lampranthus deltoides

Osmunda regalis L.   Royal Fern

Otanthus maritimus (L.) Hoffmanns.
    & Link   Cottonweed

Oxalis acetosella L.   Wood-sorrel
  articulata Savigny   Pink-sorrel
  corniculata L.   Procumbent Yellow-sorrel
  corymbosa DC.   Large-flowered Pink-sorrel
  europaea Jordan   Upright Yellow-sorrel
  exilis A. Cunn.   Least Y.
  incarnata L.   Pale Pink-sorrel
  latifolia Kunth   Garden P.
  pes-caprae L.   Bermuda-buttercup
  stricta auct. non L. <u>see</u> O. europaea

Oxyria digyna (L.) Hill   Mountain Sorrel

Oxytropis campestris (L.) DC.   Yellow Oxytropis
  halleri Koch   Purple O.

Paeonia mascula (L.) Miller   Peony

Panicum miliaceum L.   Common Millet

Papaver argemone L.   Prickly Poppy
  atlanticum (Ball) Cosson   Atlas P.
  dubium L.   Long-headed P.
  hybridum L.   Rough P.
  lecoqii Lamotte   Yellow-juiced P.
  rhoeas L.   Common P.
  somniferum L.   Opium P.

Parapholis incurva (L.) C.E. Hubbard   Curved Hard-grass
  strigosa (Dumort.) C.E. Hubbard   Hard-grass

Parentucellia viscosa (L.) Caruel   Yellow Bartsia

Parietaria diffusa Mert. & Koch see
    P. judaica
  judaica L.   Pellitory-of-the-wall

Paris quadrifolia L.   Herb-Paris

Parnassia palustris L.   Grass-of-Parnassus

Pastinaca sativa L.   Wild Parsnip

Pedicularis palustris L.   Marsh Lousewort
  sylvatica L.   Lousewort

Pentaglottis sempervirens (L.)
    L.H. Bailey   Green Alkanet

Peplis portula L. see Lythrum portula

Pernettya mucronata (L. fil.) Gaudich.   Prickly Heath

Petasites albus (L.) Gaertner   White Butterbur
  fragrans (Vill.) C. Presl   Winter Heliotrope
  hybridus (L.) P. Gaertner, B.
    Meyer & Scherb   Butterbur
  japonicus (Siebold & Zucc.) Maxim.   Giant B.

Petrorhagia nanteuilii (Burnat)
    P.W. Ball & Heywood   Childing Pink
  prolifera (L.) P.W. Ball & Heywood   Proliferous P.

Petroselinum crispum (Miller) A.W. Hill   Garden Parsley
  segetum (L.) Koch   Corn P.

Peucedanum officinale

Peucedanum officinale L.	Hog's Fennel
ostruthium (L.) Koch	Masterwort
palustre (L.) Moench	Milk-parsley
Phalaris arundinacea L.	Reed Canary-grass
canariensis L.	Canary-grass
minor Retz	Lesser C.
paradoxa L.	Awned C.
Phegopteris connectilis (Michx) Watt	Beech Fern
Phleum alpinum L.	Alpine Cat's-tail
arenarium L.	Sand C.
bertolonii DC. see Phleum	
pratense subsp. bertolonii	
phleoides (L.) Karsten	Purple-stem C.
pratense L.	
subsp. bertolonii (DC.) Serb. &	
Nyarady	Smaller C.
subsp. pratense	Timothy
Phormium tenax J.R. & G. Forster	New Zealand-flax
Phragmites australis (Cav.) Steudel	Common Reed
communis Trin. see P. australis	
Phlomis fruticosa L.	Jerusalem Sage
Phyllitis scolopendrium (L.) Newman	Hart's-tongue
Phyllodoce caerulea (L.) Bab.	Blue Heath
Physalis alkekengi L.	Japanese-lantern
Physospermum cornubiense (L.) DC.	Bladderseed
Phyteuma orbiculare L.	Round-headed Rampion
spicatum L.	Spiked R.
tenerum R. Schulz see P. orbiculare	
Picea abies (L.) Karsten	Norway Spruce
sitchensis (Bong.) Carrière	Sitka S.
Picris echioides L.	Bristly Oxtongue
hieracioides L.	Hawkweed O.
Pilosella see Hieracium	
Pilularia globulifera L.	Pillwort
Pimpinella major (L.) Hudson	Greater Burnet-saxifrage
saxifraga L.	Burnet-saxifrage
Pinguicula grandiflora Lam.	Large-flowered Butterwort
lusitanica L.	Pale B.
vulgaris L.	Common B.

42

Pinus nigra Arnold
    subsp. laricio (Poiret) Palibin   Corsican Pine
    subsp. nigra   Austrian P.
    pinaster Aiton   Maritime P.
    radiata Aiton   Monterey P.
    sylvestris L.   Scots P.

Pittosporum crassifolium A. Cunn.   Karo

Plantago arenaria Waldst. & Kit.   Branched Plantain
    coronopus L.   Buck's-horn P.
    indica auct. see P. arenaria
    lanceolata L.   Ribwort P.
    major L.   Greater P.
    maritima L.   Sea P.
    media L.   Hoary P.

Platanthera bifolia (L.)
    L.C.M. Richard   Lesser Butterfly-orchid
    chlorantha (Custer) Reichenb.   Greater B.

Platanus x hybrida Brot.   London Plane

Poa alpina L.   Alpine Meadow-grass
    angustifolia L.   Narrow-leaved M.
    annua L.   Annual M.
    bulbosa L.   Bulbous M.
    chaixii Vill.   Broad-leaved M.
    compressa L.   Flattened M.
    flexuosa Sm.   Wavy M.
    glauca Vahl   Glaucous M.
    infirma Kunth   Early M.
    nemoralis L.   Wood M.
    palustris L.   Swamp M.
    pratensis L.   Smooth M.
    pratensis L. subsp. angustifolia
      see P. angustifolia
    subcaerulea Sm.   Spreading M.
    trivialis L.   Rough M.

Polemonium caeruleum L.   Jacob's-ladder

Polycarpon tetraphyllum (L.) L.   Four-leaved Allseed

Polygala amara L. see P. amarella
    amarella Crantz   Dwarf Milkwort
    calcarea F.W. Schultz   Chalk M.
    serpyllifolia J.A.C. Hose   Heath M.
    vulgaris L.   Common M.

Polygonatum multiflorum (L.) All.   Solomon's-seal
    odoratum (Miller) Druce   Angular S.
    verticillatum (L.) All.   Whorled S.

Polygonum aequale Lindm. see P.
    arenastrum

Polygonum alpinum

Polygonum - continued
alpinum All.	Alpine Knotweed
amphibium L.	Amphibious Bistort
amplexicaule D. Don	Red B.
arenastrum Boreau	Equal-leaved Knotgrass
aubertii Louis Henry see Fallopia aubertii	
aviculare L.	Knotgrass
baldschuanicum Regel see Fallopia baldschuanica	
bistorta L.	Common Bistort
boreale (Lange) Small	Northern Knotgrass
campanulatum Hooker fil.	Lesser Knotweed
convolvulus L. see Fallopia convolvulus	
cuspidatum Siebold & Zucc. see Reynoutria japonica	
dumetorum L. see Fallopia dumetorum	
hydropiper L.	Water-pepper
lapathifolium L.	Pale Persicaria
maritimum L.	Sea Knotgrass
minus Hudson	Small Water-pepper
mite Schrank	Tasteless W.
oxyspermum Ledeb. subsp. raii (Bab.) D.A. Webb & Chater	Ray's Knotgrass
pensylvanicum L.	Pinkweed
persicaria L.	Redshank
polystachyum Meissner	Himalayan Knotweed
raii Bab. see P. oxyspermum subsp. raii	
rurivagum Boreau	Cornfield Knotgrass
sachalinense Friedrich Schmidt Petrop. see Reynoutria sachalinense	
sagittatum L.	American Tear-thumb
sieboldii hort. see Reynoutria japonica	
viviparum L.	Alpine Bistort

Polypodium australe Fee see P. cambricum	
cambricum L.	Southern Polypody
interjectum Shivas	Intermediate P.
vulgare L.	Polypody

Polypogon monspeliensis (L.) Desf.	Annual Beard-grass
semiverticillatus (Forsskål) Hyl.	Water Bent

Polystichum aculeatum (L.) Roth	Hard Shield-fern
lonchitis (L.) Roth	Holly Fern
setiferum (Forsskål) Woynar	Soft Shield-fern

Populus alba L.	White Poplar
x canadensis Moench var. serotina (Hartig) Rehder	Italian P.
candicans Aiton	Balm-of-Gilead
x canescens (Aiton) Sm.	Grey Poplar
x gileadensis Rouleau see P. candicans	

Populus - continued
nigra L.   Black Poplar
nigra L. var. italica Muenchh.   Lombardy P.
tremula L.   Aspen
trichocarpa Torrey & A. Gray   Western Balsam-poplar

Portulaca oleracea L.   Common Purslane

Potamogeton acutifolius Link   Sharp-leaved Pondweed
alpinus Balbis   Red P.
berchtoldii Fieber   Small P.
coloratus Hornem.   Fen P.
compressus L.   Grass-wrack P.
crispus L.   Curled P.
epihydrus Rafin.   American P.
filiformis Pers.   Slender-leaved P.
friesii Rupr.   Flat-stalked P.
gramineus L.   Various-leaved P.
lucens L.   Shining P.
natans L.   Broad-leaved P.
nodosus Poiret   Loddon P.
obtusifolius Mert. & Koch   Blunt-leaved P.
panormitanus Biv. see P. pusillus
pectinatus L.   Fennel P.
perfoliatus L.   Perfoliate P.
polygonifolius Pourret   Bog P.
praelongus Wulfen   Long-stalked P.
pusillus auct., non L. see
     P. berchtoldii
pusillus L.   Lesser P.
rutilus Wolfg.   Shetland P.
trichoides Cham. & Schlecht.   Hairlike P.

Potentilla anglica Laicharding   Trailing Tormentil
anserina L.   Silverweed
argentea L.   Hoary Cinquefoil
crantzii (Crantz) Fritsch   Alpine C.
erecta (L.) Rauschel   Tormentil
fruticosa L.   Shrubby Cinquefoil
norvegica L.   Ternate-leaved C.
palustris (L.) Scop.   Marsh C.
recta L.   Sulphur C.
reptans L.   Creeping C.
rupestris L.   Rock C.
sterilis (L.) Garcke   Barren Strawberry
tabernaemontani Ascherson   Spring Cinquefoil

Poterium polygamum Waldst. & Kit.
     see Sanguisorba minor
sanguisorba L. see Sanguisorba minor

Primula elatior (L.) Hill   Oxlip
farinosa L.   Bird's-eye Primrose
scotica Hooker   Scottish P.
veris L.   Cowslip
veris x P. vulgaris   False Oxlip

<u>Primula</u> <u>vulgaris</u>

Primula - <u>continued</u>
  vulgaris Hudson   Primrose

Prunella laciniata (L.) L.   Cut-leaved Selfheal
  vulgaris L.   Selfheal

Prunus avium (L.) L.   Wild Cherry
  cerasifera Ehrh.   Cherry Plum
  cerasus L.   Dwarf Cherry
  domestica L.   Wild Plum
  laurocerasus L.   Cherry Laurel
  lusitanica L.   Portugal L.
  padus L.   Bird Cherry
  spinosa L.   Blackthorn

Pseudorchis albida (L.) Á.& D. Löve   Small-white Orchid

Pseudotsuga menziesii (Mirb.) Franco   Douglas Fir

Pteridium aquilinum (L.) Kuhn   Bracken

Puccinellia capillaris (Liljeblad)
    Jansen <u>see</u> P. distans
      subsp. borealis
    distans (Jacq.) Parl.
      subsp. distans   Reflexed Saltmarsh-grass
      subsp. borealis (Holmberg)
        W.E. Hughes   Northern S.
    fasciculata (Torrey) Bicknell   Borrer's S.
    maritima (Hudson) Parl.   Common S.
    pseudodistans (Crép.) Jansen & Wacht. Greater S.
    rupestris (With.) Fernald & Weatherby Stiff S.

Pulicaria dysenterica (L.) Bernh.   Common Fleabane
  vulgaris Gaertner   Small F.

Pulmonaria longifolia (Bast.) Boreau   Narrow-leaved Lungwort
  officinalis L.   Lungwort

Pulsatilla vulgaris Miller   Pasqueflower

Pyrola media Swartz   Intermediate Wintergreen
  minor L.   Common W.
  rotundifolia L.   Round-leaved W.

Pyrus communis auct. <u>see</u> P. pyraster
  cordata Desv.   Plymouth Pear
  pyraster Burgsd.   Wild P.

Quercus borealis Michx fil. var.
    maxima (Marsh) Ashe   Red Oak
  cerris L.   Turkey O.
  ilex L.   Evergreen O.

46

Quercus - continued
  petraea (Mattuschka) Liebl.   Sessile Oak
  robur L.   Pedunculate O.

Radiola linoides Roth   Allseed

Ranunculus acris L.   Meadow Buttercup
  aquatilis L.   Common Water-crowfoot
  arvensis L.   Corn Buttercup
  auricomus L.   Goldilocks B.
  baudotii Godron   Brackish Water-crowfoot
  bulbosus L.   Bulbous Buttercup
  circinatus Sibth.   Fan-leaved Water-crowfoot
  ficaria L.   Lesser Celandine
  flammula L.   Lesser Spearwort
  fluitans Lam.   River Water-crowfoot
  hederaceus L.   Ivy-leaved Crowfoot
  lingua L.   Greater Spearwort
  marginatus D' Urv.   St Martin's Buttercup
  muricatus L.   Rough-fruited B.
  omiophyllus Ten.   Round-leaved Crowfoot
  ophioglossifolius Vill.   Adder's-tongue Spearwort
  paludosus Poiret   Jersey Buttercup
  parviflorus L.   Small-flowered B.
  peltatus Schrank   Pond Water-crowfoot
  penicillatus (Dumort.) Bab.   Stream W.
  repens L.   Creeping Buttercup
  reptans L.   Creeping Spearwort
  sardous Crantz   Hairy Buttercup
  sceleratus L.   Celery-leaved B.
  trichophyllus Chaix   Thread-leaved
                               Water-crowfoot
  tripartitus DC.   Three-lobed Crowfoot

Raphanus maritimus Sm.   Sea Radish
  raphanistrum L.   Wild R.
  sativus L.   Garden R.

Rapistrum perenne (L.) All.   Steppe Cabbage
  rugosum (L.) All.   Bastard C.

Reseda alba L.   White Mignonette
  lutea L.   Wild M.
  luteola L.   Weld

Reynoutria japonica Houtt.   Japanese Knotweed
  sachalinensis (Friedrich Schmidt
    Petrop) Nakai   Giant K.

Rhamnus catharticus L.   Buckthorn

Rheum rhabarbarum L.   Rhubarb

Rhinanthus angustifolius C.C. Gmelin   Greater Yellow-rattle
  minor L.   Yellow-rattle

Rhinanthus _serotinus_

Rhinanthus - _continued_
  serotinus (Schonheit) Oborny _see_
    R. angustifolius

Rhododendron ponticum L.   Rhododendron

Rhynchosinapis cheiranthos (Vill.) Dandy   Wallflower Cabbage
  monensis (L.) Clapham   Isle of Man C.
  wrightii (O.E. Schultz) Clapham   Lundy C.

Rhynchospora alba (L.) Vahl   White Beak-sedge
  fusca (L.) Aiton fil.   Brown B.

Ribes alpinum L.   Mountain Currant
  nigrum L.   Black C.
  rubrum L.   Red C.
  sanguineum Pursh   Flowering C.
  spicatum Robson   Downy C.
  uva-crispa L.   Gooseberry

Robinia pseudacacia L.   False-acacia

Roemeria hybrida (L.) DC.   Violet Horned-poppy

Romulea columnae Sebastiani & Mauri   Sand Crocus

Rorippa amphibia (L.) Besser   Great Yellow-cress
  austriaca (Crantz) Besser   Austrian Y.
  islandica (Murray) Borbás   Northern Y.
  microphylla (Boenn.) Hyland. _see_
    Nasturtium microphylla
  nasturtium-aquaticum (L.) Hayek
    see Nasturtium officinale
  palustris (L.) Besser   Marsh Y.
  sylvestris (L.) Besser   Creeping Y.
x sterilis Airy Shaw _see_ Nasturtium
    x sterile

Rosa afzeliana Fries   Glaucous Dog-rose
  agrestis Savi   Small-leaved Sweet-briar
  arvensis Hudson   Field-rose
  caesia Sm. _see_ R. coriifolia
  canina L.   Dog-rose
  coriifolia Fries   Hairy Dog-rose
  corymbifera Borkh. _see_ R. dumetorum
  dumalis Bechst. _see_ R. afzeliana
  dumetorum Thuill.   Thicket Dog-rose
  eglanteria L. _see_ R. rubiginosa L.
  micrantha Sm.   Small-flowered
                                                            Sweet-briar
  mollis Sm.   Soft Downy-rose
  multiflora Thunb.   Many-flowered Rose
  obtusifolia Desv.   Round-leaved Dog-rose
  pimpinellifolia L.   Burnet Rose
  rubiginosa L.   Sweet-briar
  rugosa Thunb.   Japanese Rose
  sherardii Davies   Sherard's Downy-rose

Rosa - continued
spinosissima L. see R. pimpinellifolia
stylosa Desv.   Short-styled Field-rose
tomentosa Sm.   Harsh Downy-rose
virginiana Miller   Virginian Rose
vosagiaca Desportes see R. afzeliana

Rubia peregrina L.   Wild Madder

Rubus caesius L.   Dewberry
chamaemorus L.   Cloudberry
fruticosus L.   Bramble
idaeus L.   Raspberry
saxatilis L.   Stone Bramble
spectabilis Pursh   Salmonberry

Rudbeckia laciniata L.   Coneflower

Rumex acetosa L.   Common Sorrel
acetosella L.   Sheep's S.
alpinus L.   Monk's-rhubarb
ambiguus Gren. see R. acetosa
angiocarpus Murb. see R. acetosella
aquaticus L.   Scottish Dock
brownii Campd.   Hooked D.
conglomeratus Murray   Clustered D.
crispus L.   Curled D.
cristatus DC.   Greek D.
domesticus Hartman see R. longifolius
fennicus (Murb.) Murb. see R.
  aquaticus
fimbriatus R. Br. see R. brownii
frutescens Thouars   Argentine D.
graecus Boiss. & Heldr. see R.
  cristatus
hibernicus Rech. fil.   Irish Sorrel
hydrolapathum Hudson   Water Dock
limosus auct. angl., non Thuill.
  see R. palustris
longifolius DC.   Northern D.
maritimus L.   Golden D.
nemorosus Willd. see R. sanguineus
obovatus Danser   Obovate-leaved D.
obtusifolius L.   Broad-leaved D.
palustris Sm.   Marsh D.
patientia L.   Patience D.
pulcher L.   Fiddle D.
rugosus Campd.   Garden Sorrel
rupestris Le Gall   Shore Dock
salicifolius auct. see R.
  triangulivalvis
sanguineus L. var. sanguineus   Blood-veined D.
  var. viridis (Sibth.) Koch   Wood D.
scutatus L.   French Sorrel
tenuifolius (Wallr.) Á. Löve   Narrow-leaved S.
triangulivalvis (Danser) Rech. fil.   Willow-leaved Dock

<u>Ruppia</u> <u>cirrhosa</u>

Ruppia cirrhosa (Petagna) Grande   Spiral Tasselweed
   maritima L.   Beaked T.
   spiralis Dumort. <u>see</u> R. cirrhosa

Ruscus aculeatus L.   Butcher's-broom

Sagina apetala Ard.   Annual Pearlwort
   intermedia Fenzl   Snow P.
   maritima G. Don fil.   Sea P.
   nodosa (L.) Fenzl   Knotted P.
x normaniana Lagerh.   Scottish P.
   procumbens L.   Procumbent P.
   saginoides (L.) Karsten   Alpine P.
   subulata (Swartz) C. Presl   Heath P.

Sagittaria rigida Pursh   Canadian Arrowhead
   sagittifolia L.   Arrowhead

Salicornia europaea L.   Glasswort
   perennis Miller   Perennial G.

Salix alba L.
     var. alba   White Willow
     var. caerulea (Sm.) Sm.   Cricket-bat W.
     var. vitellina (L.) Stokes   Golden W.
   amygdalina L. <u>see</u> S. triandra
   aquatica Sm. <u>see</u> S. cinerea
     subsp. cinerea
   arbuscula L.   Mountain W.
   arenaria L. sec. Sm. <u>see</u> S. lapponum
   arenaria L. sec. Flod. <u>see</u> S. repens
   atrocinerea Brot. <u>see</u> S. cinerea
     subsp. oleifolia
   aurita L.   Eared W.
   caprea L.   Goat W.
   cinerea L.
     subsp. cinerea   Grey W.
     subsp. oleifolia Macreight   Rusty W.
   decipiens Hoffm. <u>see</u> S. fragilis
     var. decipiens
   fragilis L.
     var. decipiens (Hoffm.) Koch   Welsh W.
     var. fragilis   Crack W.
     var. russelliana (Sm.) Koch   Bedford W.
   helix L. <u>see</u> S. purpurea
   herbacea L.   Dwarf W.
   hibernica Rech. f. <u>see</u> S. phylicifolia
   lambertiana Sm. <u>see</u> S. purpurea
   lanata L.   Woolly W.
   lapponum L.   Downy W.
   myrsinifolia Salisb.   Dark-leaved W.
   myrsinites L.   Whortle-leaved W.
   nigricans Sm. <u>see</u> S. myrsinifolia

Salix - continued
  pentandra L.   Bay Willow
  phylicifolia L.   Tea-leaved W.
  purpurea L.   Purple W.
  repens L.   Creeping W.
  reticulata L.   Net-leaved W.
  stuartiana Sm. see S. lapponum
  triandra L.   Almond W.
  viminalis L.   Osier
  woolgariana Sm. see S. purpurea

Salpichroa origanifolia (Lam.) Baillon   Cock's-eggs

Salsola kali L.
    subsp. kali   Prickly Saltwort
    subsp. ruthenica (Iljin) Soó   Spineless S.
  pestifer A. Nelson see S. kali
    subsp. ruthenica

Salvia horminoides Pourret see S.
  verbenaca
  pratensis L.   Meadow Clary
  reflexa Hornem.   Mintweed
  verbenaca L.   Wild Clary
  verticillata L.   Whorled C.

Sambucus ebulus L.   Dwarf Elder
  nigra L.   Elder
  racemosa L.   Red-berried E.

Samolus valerandi L.   Brookweed

Sanguisorba minor Scop.
    subsp. minor   Salad Burnet
    subsp. muricata Briq.   Fodder B.
  officinalis L.   Great B.

Sanicula europaea L.   Sanicle

Saponaria officinalis L.   Soapwort

Sarothamnus scoparius (L.) Wimmer
  see Cytisus scoparius

Sarracenia purpurea L.   Pitcherplant

Satureja montana L.   Winter Savory

Saussurea alpina (L.) DC.   Alpine Saw-wort

Saxifraga aizoides L.   Yellow Saxifrage
  cernua L.   Drooping S.
  cespitosa L.   Tufted S.
  cymbalaria L.   Celandine S.
  granulata L.   Meadow S.
  hirculus L.   Marsh S.

Saxifraga - continued
  hirsuta L.   Kidney Saxifrage
  hypnoides L.   Mossy S.
  nivalis L.   Alpine S.
  oppositifolia L.   Purple S.
  rivularis L.   Highland S.
  rosacea Moench   Irish S.
  spathularis Brot.   St Patrick's-cabbage
  spathularis Brot. x umbrosa L. see
    S. urbium
  stellaris L.   Starry Saxifrage
  tridactylites L.   Rue-leaved S.
  umbrosa L.   Pyrenean S.
x urbium D.A. Webb   Londonpride

Scabiosa columbaria L.   Small Scabious

Scandix pecten-veneris L.   Shepherd's-needle

Scheuchzeria palustris L.   Rannoch-rush

Schoenoplectus americanus (Pers.)
    Volkart see S. pungens
  lacustris (L.) Palla   Common Club-rush
  pungens (Vahl) Palla   Sharp C.
  tabernaemontani (C.C. Gmelin) Palla   Grey C.
  triqueter (L.) Palla   Triangular C.

Schoenus ferrugineus L.   Brown Bog-rush
  nigricans L.   Black B.

Scilla autumnalis L.   Autumn Squill
  verna Hudson   Spring S.

Scirpus americanus auct. eur., non
    Pers. see Schoenoplectus pungens
  caespitosus L. see Trichophorum
    cespitosum
  cernuus Vahl see Isolepis cernua
  fluitans L. see Eleogiton fluitans
  holoschoenus L. see Holoschoenus
    vulgaris
  lacustris L. see Schoenoplectus
    lacustris
  maritimus L.   Sea Club-rush
  setaceus L. see Isolepis setacea
  sylvaticus L.   Wood C.
  tabernaemontani C.C. Gmelin see
    Schoenoplectus tabernaemontani
  triqueter L. see Schoenoplectus
    triqueter

Scleranthus annuus L.   Annual Knawel
  perennis L.   Perennial K.

Scorzonera humilis L.   Viper's-grass

Scrophularia aquatica auct., non
  L. see S. auriculata
  auriculata L.   Water Figwort
  nodosa L.   Common F.
  scorodonia L.   Balm-leaved F.
  umbrosa Dumort.   Green F.
  vernalis L.   Yellow F.

Scutellaria galericulata L.   Skullcap
  hastifolia L.   Norfolk S.
  minor L.   Lesser S.

Sedum acre L.   Biting Stonecrop
  album L.   White S.
  anglicum Hudson   English S.
  dasyphyllum L.   Thick-leaved S.
  forsterianum L.   Rock S.
  reflexum L.   Reflexed S.
  rosea (L.) Scop.   Roseroot
  spurium M. Bieb.   Caucasian S.
  sexangulare L.   Tasteless Stonecrop
  telephium L.   Orpine
  villosum L.   Hairy Stonecrop

Selaginella kraussiana (G. Kunze)
  A. Braun   Krauss's Clubmoss
  selaginoides (L.) Link   Lesser C.

Selinum carvifolia (L.) L.   Cambridge Milk-parsley

Sempervivum tectorum L.   House-leek

Senecio aquaticus Hill   Marsh Ragwort
  bicolor (Willd.) Tod.   Silver R.
  cambrensis Rosser   Welsh Groundsel
  cineraria DC. see S. bicolor
  doria L.   Golden Ragwort
  erucifolius L.   Hoary R.
  fluviatilis Wallr.   Broad-leaved R.
  integrifolius (L.) Clairv.   Field Fleawort
  jacobaea L.   Common Ragwort
  paludosus L.   Fen R.
  palustris (L.) Hooker   Marsh Fleawort
  smithii DC.   Magellan Ragwort
  squalidus L.   Oxford R.
  sylvaticus L.   Heath Groundsel
  viscosus L.   Sticky G.
  vulgaris L.   Groundsel

Serratula tinctoria L.   Saw-wort

Seseli libanotis (L.) Koch   Moon Carrot

Sesleria albicans Schultes   Blue Moor-grass
  caerulea (L.) Ard. subsp. calcarea
    (Celak.) Hegi see S. albicans

Setaria *italica*

Setaria italica (L.) Beauv.	Foxtail Bristle-grass
lutescens (Weigel) F.T. Hubbard	
see S. pumila	
pumila (Poiret) Schultes	Yellow B.
verticillata (L.) Beauv.	Rough B.
viridis (L.) Beauv.	Green B.
Sherardia arvensis L.	Field Madder
Sibbaldia procumbens L.	Sibbaldia
Sibthorpia europaea L.	Cornish Moneywort
Sieglingia decumbens (L.) Bernh.	
see Danthonia decumbens	
Silaum silaus (L.) Schinz & Thell.	Pepper-saxifrage
Silene acaulis (L.) Jacq.	Moss Campion
alba (Miller) E.H.L. Krause	White C.
armeria L.	Sweet-William Catchfly
conica L.	Sand C.
dichotoma Ehrh.	Forked C.
dioica (L.) Clairv.	Red Campion
gallica L.	Small-flowered Catchfly
italica (L.) Pers.	Italian C.
maritima With.	Sea Campion
noctiflora L.	Night-flowering Catchfly
nutans L.	Nottingham C.
otites (L.) Wibel	Spanish C.
vulgaris (Moench) Garcke	Bladder Campion
Silybum marianum (L.) Gaertner	Milk Thistle
Simethis planifolia (L.) Gren.	Kerry Lily
Sinapis alba L.	White Mustard
arvensis L.	Charlock
Sison amomum L.	Stone Parsley
Sisymbrium altissimum L.	Tall Rocket
irio L.	London-rocket
loeselii L.	False L.
officinale (L.) Scop.	Hedge Mustard
orientale L.	Eastern Rocket
strictissimum L.	Perennial R.
Sisyrinchium bermudiana L.	Blue-eyed-grass
californicum (Ker-Gawler) Aiton fil.	Yellow-eyed-grass
montanum E.L. Greene	American Blue-eyed-grass
Sium latifolium L.	Greater Water-parsnip
Smyrnium olusatrum L.	Alexanders
perfoliatum L.	Perfoliate A.

Solanum dulcamara L.	Bittersweet
nigrum L.	Black Nightshade
sarrachoides Sendtner	Green N.
triflorum Nutt.	Three-flowered N.
Soleirolia soleirolii (Req.) Dandy	Mind-your-own-business
Solidago canadensis L.	Canadian Goldenrod
gigantea Aiton	Early G.
virgaurea L.	Goldenrod
Sonchus arvensis L.	Perennial Sow-thistle
asper (L.) Hill	Prickly S.
oleraceus L.	Smooth S.
palustris L.	Marsh S.
Sorbus aria (L.) Crantz	Common Whitebeam
aucuparia L.	Rowan
domestica L.	Service-tree
intermedia (Ehrh.) Pers.	Swedish Whitebeam
latifolia (Lam.) Pers.	Broad-leaved W.
rupicola (Syme) Hedl.	Rock W.
torminalis (L.) Crantz	Wild Service-tree
Sparganium angustifolium Michx	Floating Bur-reed
emersum Rehmann	Unbranched B.
erectum L.	Branched B.
minimum Wallr.	Least B.
Spartina alterniflora Loisel.	Smooth Cord-grass
anglica C.E. Hubbard	Common C.
maritima (Curtis) Fernald	Small C.
x townsendii H. & J. Groves	Townsend's C.
Spartium junceum L.	Spanish Broom
Spergula arvensis L.	Corn Spurrey
Spergularia bocconii (Scheele)	
Ascherson & Graebner	Greek Sea-spurrey
marina (L.) Griseb.	Lesser S.
media (L.) C. Presl	Greater S.
rubra (L.) J. & C. Presl	Sand Spurrey
rupicola Le Jolis	Rock Sea-spurrey
Spiraea salicifolia L.	Bridewort
Spiranthes aestivalis (Poiret)	
L.C.M. Richard	Summer Lady's-tresses
romanzoffiana Cham.	Irish L.
spiralis (L.) Chevall.	Autumn L.
Stachys alpina L.	Limestone Woundwort
arvensis (L.) L.	Field W.
germanica L.	Downy W.
officinalis (L.) Trev.	Betony

Stachys - continued
  palustris L.   Marsh Woundwort
  sylvatica L.   Hedge W.

Stellaria alsine Grimm   Bog Stitchwort
  graminea L.   Lesser S.
  holostea L.   Greater S.
  media (L.) Vill.   Common Chickweed
  neglecta Weihe   Greater C.
  nemorum L.   Wood Stitchwort
  pallida (Dumort.) Pire   Lesser Chickweed
  palustris Retz.   Marsh Stitchwort

Stratiotes aloides L.   Water-soldier

Suaeda fruticosa auct. see S. vera
  maritima (L.) Dumort.   Annual Sea-blite
  vera J.R. Gmelin   Shrubby S.

Subularia aquatica L.   Awlwort

Succisa pratensis Moench   Devils'-bit Scabious

Swida sanguinea (L.) Opiz see
  Cornus sanguinea

Symphoricarpos rivularis Suksdorf   Snowberry

Symphytum asperum Lepechin   Rough Comfrey
  bulbosum C. Schimper   Bulbous C.
  grandiflorum auct., non DC. see
    S. ibiricum
  ibericum Steven   Creeping C.
  officinale L.   Common C.
  orientale L.   White C.
  tauricum Willd.   Crimean C.
  tuberosum L.   Tuberous C.
x uplandicum Nyman   Russian C.

Syringa vulgaris L.   Lilac

Tamarix anglica Webb see T. gallica
  gallica L.   Tamarisk

Tamus communis L.   Black Bryony

Tanacetum parthenium (L.) Schulz Bip.   Feverfew
  vulgare L.   Tansy

Taraxacum laevigatum (Willd.) DC.   Lesser Dandelion
  officinale Weber   Common Dandelion
  palustre (Lyons) DC.   Narrow-leaved
                              Marsh-dandelion
  spectabile Dahlst.   Red-veined Dandelion

Taxus baccata L.   Yew

Teesdalia nudicaulis (L.) R. Br.   Shepherd's Cress

Tellima grandiflora (Pursh) Lindley   Fringe-cups

Tetragonolobus maritimus (L.) Roth   Dragon's-teeth

Teucrium botrys L.   Cut-leaved Germander
    chamaedrys L.   Wall G.
    scordium L.   Water G.
    scorodonia L.   Wood Sage

Thalictrum alpinum L.   Alpine Meadow-rue
    flavum L.   Common M.
    minus L.   Lesser M.

Thelycrania sanguinea (L.) Fourr.
    see Cornus sanguinea

Thelypteris dryopteris (L.) Slosson
    see Gymnocarpium dryopteris
    limbosperma (All.) H.P. Fuchs
      see Oreopteris limbosperma
    oreopteris (Ehrh.) Slosson see
      Oreopteris limbosperma
    palustris Schott   Marsh Fern
    phegopteris (L.) Slosson see
      Phegopteris connectilis
    robertiana (Hoffm.) Slosson see
      Gymnocarpium robertianum
    thelypteroides Michx see T. palustris

Thesium humifusum DC.   Bastard-toadflax

Thlaspi alliaceum L.   Garlic Penny-cress
    alpestre L.   Alpine P.
    arvense L.   Field P.
    perfoliatum L.   Perfoliate P.

Thymus drucei Ronniger see T.
      praecox subsp. arcticus
    praecox Opiz subsp. arcticus
      (Durand) Jalas   Wild Thyme
    pulegioides L.   Large T.
    serpyllum L.   Breckland T.

Tilia cordata Miller   Small-leaved Lime
    platyphyllos Scop.   Large-leaved L.
x vulgaris Hayne   Lime

Tillaea aquatica L. see Crassula
      aquatica
    muscosa L. see Crassula tillaea

Tofieldia pusilla (Michx) Pers.   Scottish Asphodel

<u>Tolmiea</u> <u>menziesii</u>

Tolmiea menziesii (Pursh) Torrey &
   A. Gray   Pick-a-back-plant

Tordylium maximum L.   Hartwort

Torilis arvense (Hudson) Link   Spreading Hedge-parsley
   japonica (Houtt.) DC.   Upright H.
   nodosa (L.) Gaertner   Knotted H.

Trachystemon orientalis (L.) D. Don   Abraham-Isaac-Jacob

Tragopogon porrifolius L.   Salsify
   pratensis L.   Goat's-beard

Trichomanes speciosum Willd.   Killarney Fern

Trichophorum cespitosum (L.) Hartman   Deergrass

Trientalis europaea L.   Chickweed Wintergreen

Trifolium arvense L.   Hare's-foot Clover
   aureum Pollich   Large Trefoil
   bocconei Savi   Twin-headed Clover
   campestre Schreber   Hop Trefoil
   dubium Sibth.   Lesser T.
   fragiferum L.   Strawberry Clover
   glomeratum L.   Clustered C.
   hybridum L.   Alsike C.
   incarnatum L.
      subsp. incarnatum   Crimson C.
      subsp. molineri (Balbis) Hooker fil.   Long-headed C.
   medium L.   Zigzag C.
   micranthum Viv.   Slender Trefoil
   molineri Hornem. <u>see</u> T. incarnatum
      subsp. molineri
   occidentale D.E. Coombe   Western Clover
   ochroleucon Hudson   Sulphur C.
   ornithopodioides L.   Bird's-foot C.
   pratense L.   Red C.
   repens L.   White C.
   resupinatum L.   Reversed C.
   scabrum L.   Rough C.
   squamosum L.   Sea C.
   stellatum L.   Starry C.
   striatum L.   Knotted C.
   strictum L.   Upright C.
   subterraneum L.   Subterranean C.
   suffocatum L.   Suffocated C.

Triglochin maritima L.   Sea Arrowgrass
   palustris L.   Marsh A.

Trinia glauca (L.) Dumort.   Honewort

Tripleurospermum inodorum Schultz Bip.   Scentless Mayweed
   maritimum (L.) Koch   Sea M.

Trisetum flavescens (L.) Beauv.	Yellow Oat-grass
Tritonia x crocosmiflora (Lemoine) Nicholson	Montbretia
Trollius europaeus L.	Globeflower
Tsuga heterophylla (Rafin.) Sargent	Western Hemlock-spruce
Tuberaria guttata (L.) Fourr.	Spotted Rock-rose
Tulipa sylvestris L.	Wild Tulip
Turgenia latifolia (L.) Hoffm.	Greater Bur-parsley
Turritis glabra L. see Arabis glabra	
Tussilago farfara L.	Colt's-foot
Typha angustifolia L. 　latifolia L.	Lesser Bulrush Bulrush

Ulex europaeus L. 　gallii Planchon 　minor Roth	Gorse Western G. Dwarf G.
Ulmus carpinifolia G.G. Suckow see 　U. minor 　glabra Hudson 　minor Miller 　procera Salisb.	 Wych Elm Small-leaved E. English E.
Umbilicus rupestris (Salisb.) Dandy	Navelwort
Urtica dioica L. 　pilulifera L. 　urens L.	Common Nettle Roman N. Small N.
Utricularia australis R. Br. 　intermedia Hayne 　minor L. 　neglecta Lehm. see U. australis 　vulgaris L.	Bladderwort Intermediate B. Lesser B. Greater B.

Vaccaria hispanica (Miller) Rauschert 　pyramidata Medicus see V. hispanica	Cowherb
Vaccinium macrocarpum Aiton 　microcarpum (Rupr.) Hooker fil. 　myrtillus L.	American Cranberry Small C. Bilberry

Vaccinium oxycoccos

Vaccinium - continued
  oxycoccos L. — Cranberry
  uliginosum L. — Bog Bilberry
  vitis-idaea L. — Cowberry

Valeriana dioica L. — Marsh Valerian
  officinalis L. — Common V.
  pyrenaica L. — Pyrenean V.

Valerianella carinata Loisel. — Keeled-fruited Cornsalad
  dentata (L.) Pollich — Narrow-fruited C.
  eriocarpa Desv. — Hairy-fruited C.
  locusta (L.) Betcke — Common C.
  rimosa Bast. — Broad-fruited C.

Vallisneria spiralis L. — Tapegrass

Verbascum blattaria L. — Moth Mullein
  lychnitis L. — White M.
  nigrum L. — Dark M.
  phlomoides L. — Orange M.
  pulverulentum Vill. — Hoary M.
  thapsus L. — Great M.
  virgatum Stokes — Twiggy M.

Verbena officinalis L. — Vervain

Veronica agrestis L. — Green Field-speedwell
  alpina L. — Alpine Speedwell
  anagallis-aquatica L. — Blue Water-speedwell
  arvensis L. — Wall Speedwell
  beccabunga L. — Brooklime
  catenata Pennell — Pink Water-speedwell
  chamaedrys L. — Germander Speedwell
  filiformis Sm. — Slender S.
  fruticans Jacq. — Rock S.
  hederifolia L. — Ivy-leaved S.
  montana L. — Wood S.
  officinalis L. — Heath S.
  peregrina L. — American S.
  persica Poiret — Common Field-speedwell
  polita Fries — Grey F.
  praecox All. — Breckland Speedwell
  repens DC. — Corsican S.
  scutellata L. — Marsh S.
  serpyllifolia L. — Thyme-leaved S.
  spicata L. — Spiked S.
  triphyllos L. — Fingered S.
  verna L. — Spring S.

Viburnum lantana L. — Wayfaring-tree
  opulus L. — Guelder-rose
  tinus L. — Laurustinus

Vicia angustifolia L. see V.
  sativa subsp. nigra

60

Vicia - continued
  bithynica (L.) L.   Bithynian Vetch
  cracca L.   Tufted V.
  faba L.   Broad Bean
  hirsuta (L.) S.F. Gray   Hairy Tare
  hybrida L.   Hairy Yellow-vetch
  lathyroides L.   Spring Vetch
  lutea L.   Yellow-vetch
  orobus DC.   Wood Bitter-vetch
  sativa L.
    subsp. sativa   Common Vetch
    subsp. nigra (L.) Ehrh.   Narrow-leaved V.
  sepium L.   Bush V.
  sylvatica L.   Wood V.
  tenuifolia Roth   Fine-leaved V.
  tenuissima (Bieb.) Schinz & Thell.   Slender Tare
  tetrasperma (L.) Schreber   Smooth T.
  villosa Roth   Fodder Vetch

Vinca major L.   Greater Periwinkle
  minor L.   Lesser P.

Viola arvensis Murray   Field Pansy
  canina L.   Heath Dog-violet
  hirta L.   Hairy Violet
  kitaibeliana Schultes   Dwarf Pansy
  lactea Sm.   Pale Dog-violet
  lutea Hudson   Mountain Pansy
  odorata L.   Sweet Violet
  palustris L.   Marsh V.
  persicifolia Schreber   Fen V.
  reichenbachiana Boreau   Early Dog-violet
  riviniana Reichenb.   Common D.
  rupestris F.W. Schmidt   Teesdale Violet
  tricolor L.   Wild Pansy

Viscum album L.   Mistletoe

Vitis vinifera L.   Grape-vine

Vulpia ambigua (Le Gall) A.G. More
    see V. ciliata subsp. ambigua
  bromoides (L.) S.F. Gray   Squirreltail Fescue
  ciliata Link subsp. ambigua
    (Le Gall) Stace & Auquier   Bearded F.
  fasciculata (Forsskål) Samp.   Dune F.
  megalura (Nutt.) Rydb.   Foxtail F.
  membranacea auct., non (L.)
    Dumort. see V. fasciculata
  myuros (L.) C.C. Gmelin   Rat's-tail F.
  unilateralis (L.) Stace   Mat-grass F.

Wahlenbergia hederacea (L.) Reichenb.   Ivy-leaved Bellflower

Wolffia arrhiza

Wolffia arrhiza (L.) Wimmer

Woodsia alpina (Bolton) S.F. Gray
   ilvensis (L.) R. Br.

Rootless Duckweed

Alpine Woodsia
Oblong W.

Xanthium spinosum L.
   strumarium L.

Spiny Cocklebur
Rough C.

Zannichellia palustris L.

Zerna erecta (Hudson) S.F. Gray
     see Bromus erectus
  ramosus (Hudson) Lindman see
     Bromus ramosus

Zostera angustifolia (Hornem.) Reichenb.
   marina L.
   noltii Hornem.

Horned Pondweed

Narrow-leaved Eelgrass
Eelgrass
Dwarf E.

Abraham-Isaac-Jacob	Trachystemon orientalis
Acacia see False-acacia	
Aconite, Winter	Eranthis hyemalis
Adder's-tongue	Ophioglossum vulgatum
Least	lusitanicum
Small	azoricum

Agrimony see also Hemp-a.

Agrimony	Agrimonia eupatoria
Bastard	Aremonia agrimonoides
Fragrant	Agrimonia procera
Alder	Alnus glutinosa
Grey	incana
Alexanders	Smyrnium olusatrum
Perfoliate	perfoliatum
Alison, Hoary	Berteroa incana
Small	Alyssum alyssoides
Sweet	Lobularia maritima
Alkanet	Anchusa officinalis
Green	Pentaglottis sempervirens
Allseed	Radiola linoides
Four-leaved	Polycarpon tetraphyllum
Alpine-clubmoss	Diphasiastrum alpinum
Hybrid	x issleri
Alpine-sedge, Black	Carex atrata
Close-headed	norvegica
Scorched	atrofusca
Amaranth, Common	Amaranthus retroflexus
Green	hybridus
White	albus
Anemone, Blue	Anemone apennina
Wood	nemorosa
Yellow	ranunculoides
Angelica, Garden	Angelica archangelica
Wild	sylvestris

Apple see also Thorn-a.

Apple, Crab	Malus sylvestris
Apple-of-Peru	Nicandra physalodes

Arabis, Garden	Arabis caucasica
Archangel, Yellow	Lamiastrum galeobdolon
Arrowgrass, Marsh	Triglochin palustris
Sea	maritima
Arrowhead	Sagittaria sagittifolia
Canadian	rigida
Arum, Bog	Calla palustris
Asarabacca	Asarum europaeum
Ash	Fraxinus excelsior
Asparagus, Garden	Asparagus officinalis
	subsp. officinalis
Wild	officinalis subsp.
	prostratus
Aspen	Populus tremula
Asphodel, Bog	Narthecium ossifragum
Scottish	Tofieldia pusilla
Aster, Goldilocks	Aster linosyris
Sea	tripolium
Astrantia	Astrantia major
Avens, Hybrid	Geum x intermedium
Mountain	Dryas octopetala
Water	Geum rivale
Wood	urbanum
Awlwort	Subularia aquatica
Azalea, Trailing	Loiseleuria procumbens
Balm	Melissa officinalis
Bastard	Melittis melissophyllum
Balm-of-Gilead	Populus candicans
Balsam, Indian	Impatiens glandulifera
Orange	capensis
Small	parviflora
Touch-me-not	noli-tangere
Balsam-poplar, Western	Populus trichocarpa
Baneberry	Actaea spicata

Barberry

Barley, Foxtail
  Meadow
  Sea
  Wall
  Wood

Bartsia, Alpine
  Red
  Yellow

Basil, Wild

Bastard-toadflax

Beak-sedge, Brown
  White

Beam see Hornbeam, Whitebeam

Bean, Broad

Bearberry
  Alpine

Beard-grass, Annual
  Perennial

Bear's-breech

Bedstraw see also Hedge-b.,
    Marsh-b.
Bedstraw, Cheddar
  Fen
  Heath
  Lady's
  Limestone
  Northern
  Slender
  Wall

Beech

Beet, Sea

Beggarticks

Bellflower, Clustered
  Creeping
  Giant
  Ivy-leaved
  Nettle-leaved
  Peach-leaved
  Rampion
  Spreading

Berberis vulgaris

Hordeum jubatum
  secalinum
  marinum
  murinum
Hordelymus europaeus

Bartsia alpina
Odontites verna
Parentucellia viscosa

Clinopodium vulgare

Thesium humifusum

Rhynchospora fusca
  alba

Vicia faba

Arctostaphylos uva-ursi
  alpinus

Polypogon monspeliensis
x Agropogon littoralis

Acanthus mollis

Galium fleurotii
  uliginosum
  saxatile
  verum
  sterneri
  boreale
  pumilum
  parisiense

Fagus sylvatica

Beta vulgaris subsp. maritima

Bidens frondosa

Campanula glomerata
  rapunculoides
  latifolia
Wahlenbergia hederacea
Campanula trachelium
  persicifolia
  rapunculus
  patula

65

Bent see also Silky-b.
Bent, Black   Agrostis gigantea
  Bristle   curtisii
  Brown   vinealis
  Common   capillaris
  Creeping   stolonifera
  Velvet   canina
  Water   Polypogon semiverticillatus

Bermuda-buttercup   Oxalis pes-caprae

Bermuda-grass   Cynodon dactylon

Betony   Stachys officinalis

Bilberry   Vaccinium myrtillus
  Bog   uliginosum

Bindweed see also Black-b.,
    Copse-b.
Bindweed, Field   Convolvulus arvensis
  Hairy   Calystegia sepium subsp.
                         pulchra
  Hedge   sepium subsp. sepium
  Large   sepium subsp. silvatica
  Sea   soldanella

Birch, Downy   Betula pubescens
  Dwarf   nana
  Silver   pendula

Bird's-foot   Ornithopus perpusillus
  Orange   pinnatus

Bird's-foot-trefoil, Common   Lotus corniculatus
  Greater   uliginosus
  Hairy   subbiflorus
  Narrow-leaved   tenuis
  Slender   angustissimus

Bird's-nest, Yellow   Monotropa hypopitys

Birthwort   Aristolochia clematitis

Bistort, Alpine   Polygonum viviparum
  Amphibious   amphibium
  Common   bistorta
  Red   amplexicaule

Bitter-cress, Hairy   Cardamine hirsuta
  Large   amara
  Narrow-leaved   impatiens
  Wavy   flexuosa

Bittersweet   Solanum dulcamara

Bitter-vetch	Lathyrus montanus
Wood	Vicia orobus
Black-bindweed	Fallopia convolvulus
Black-grass	Alopecurus myosuroides
Blackthorn	Prunus spinosa
Bladder-fern, Brittle	Cystopteris fragilis
Dickie's	dickieana
Mountain	montana
Bladder-sedge	Carex vesicaria
Mountain	saxatilis x vesicaria
Bladderseed	Physospermum cornubiense
Bladder-senna	Colutea arborescens
Bladderwort	Utricularia australis
Greater	vulgaris
Intermediate	intermedia
Lesser	minor
Blinks	Montia fontana
Blite <u>see</u> Sea-b.,	
Strawberry-b.	
Blood-drop-emlets	Mimulus luteus
Bluebell	Hyacinthoides non-scripta
Spanish	hispanica
Blue-eyed-grass	Sisyrinchium bermudiana
American	montanum
Blue-eyed-Mary	Omphalodes verna
Blue-sow-thistle, Alpine	Cicerbita alpina
Common	macrophylla
Pontic	bourgaei
Bogbean	Menyanthes trifoliata
Bog-myrtle	Myrica gale
Bog-rosemary	Andromeda polifolia
Bog-rush, Black	Schoenus nigricans
Brown	ferrugineus
Bog-sedge	Carex limosa
Mountain	rariflora
Tall	magellanica

Borage

Borage	Borago officinalis
Box	Buxus sempervirens
Bracken	Pteridium aquilinum
Bramble	Rubus fruticosus*
Stone	saxatilis
Briar see Sweet-b.	
Bridewort	Spiraea salicifolia
Bristle-grass, Foxtail	Setaria italica
Green	viridis
Rough	verticillata
Yellow	pumila
Brome see also Hairy-b.,	
Soft-b.	
Brome, Barren	Bromus sterilis
California	carinatus
Compact	madritensis
Drooping	tectorum
False	Brachypodium sylvaticum
Field	Bromus arvensis
Great	diandrus
Hungarian	inermis
Interrupted	interruptus
Meadow	commutatus
Rescue	willdenowii
Ripgut	rigidus
Rye	secalinus
Smith's	pseudosecalinus
Smooth	racemosus
Upright	erectus
Brooklime	Veronica beccabunga
Brookweed	Samolus valerandi
Broom see also Butcher's-b.	
Broom	Cytisus scoparius subsp.
	scoparius
Hairy-fruited	striatus
Prostrate	scoparius subsp. maritimus
Spanish	Spartium junceum
Broomrape, Bedstraw	Orobanche caryophyllacea
Carrot	maritima
Common	minor
Greater	rapum-genistae

---

* There are numerous microspecies which, if correctly identified,
should be so indicated.

Broomrape - <u>continued</u>
    Hemp   Orobanche ramosa
    Ivy   hederae
    Knapweed   elatior
    Oxtongue   loricata
    Thistle   reticulata
    Thyme   alba
    Yarrow   purpurea

Bryony, Black   Tamus communis
    White   Bryonia dioica

Buckler-fern, Broad   Dryopteris dilatata
    Crested   cristata
    Hay-scented   aemula
    Narrow   carthusiana
    Northern   expansa
    Rigid   villarii

Buckthorn <u>see also</u> Sea-b.
Buckthorn   Rhamnus catharticus
    Alder   Frangula alnus

Buckwheat   Fagopyrum esculentum
    Green   tataricum

Bugle   Ajuga reptans
    Pyramidal   pyramidalis

Bugloss <u>see also</u> Viper's-b.
Bugloss   Anchusa arvensis

Bullwort   Ammi majus

Bulrush   Typha latifolia
    Lesser   angustifolia

Bur <u>see</u> Pirri-pirri-bur

Burdock, Greater   Arctium lappa
    Lesser   minus*

Bur-marigold, Nodding   Bidens cernua
    Trifid   tripartita

Burnet, Fodder   Sanguisorba minor
                                        subsp. muricata
    Great   officinalis
    Salad   minor subsp. minor

Burnet-saxifrage   Pimpinella saxifraga
    Greater   major

---

* There are closely allied species which, if correctly identified,
should be so indicated.

Bur-parsley, Greater

Bur-parsley, Greater	Turgenia latifolia
Small	Caucalis platycarpos
Bur-reed, Branched	Sparganium erectum
Floating	angustifolium
Least	minimum
Unbranched	emersum
Butcher's-broom	Ruscus aculeatus
Butterbur	Petasites hybridus
Giant	japonicus
White	albus
Buttercup see also	
Bermuda-b.	
Buttercup, Bulbous	Ranunculus bulbosus
Celery-leaved	sceleratus
Corn	arvensis
Creeping	repens
Goldilocks	auricomus
Hairy	sardous
Jersey	paludosus
Meadow	acris
Rough-fruited	muricatus
St Martin's	marginatus
Small-flowered	parviflorus
Butterfly-bush	Buddleja davidii
Butterfly-orchid, Greater	Platanthera chlorantha
Lesser	bifolia
Butterwort, Common	Pinguicula vulgaris
Large-flowered	grandiflora
Pale	lusitanica
Buttonweed	Cotula coronopifolia

Cabbage see also St	
Patrick's-c., Warty-c.	
Cabbage, Bastard	Rapistrum rugosum
Isle of Man	Rhynchosinapis monensis
Lundy	wrightii
Steppe	Rapistrum perenne
Wallflower	Rhynchosinapis cheiranthos
Wild	Brassica oleracea
Calamint, Common	Calamintha sylvatica subsp.
	ascendens
Lesser	nepeta
Wood	sylvatica subsp. sylvatica

Campion, Bladder	Silene vulgaris
Moss	acaulis
Red	dioica
Sea	maritima
White	alba
Canary-grass	Phalaris canariensis
Awned	paradoxa
Lesser	minor
Reed	arundinacea
Candytuft, Garden	Iberis umbellata
Wild	amara
Canterbury-bells	Campanula medium
Caraway	Carum carvi
Whorled	verticillatum
Carrot, Moon	Seseli libanotis
Sea	Daucus carota subsp. gummifer
Wild	carota subsp. carota
Catchfly, Alpine	Lychnis alpina
Berry	Cucubalus baccifer
Forked	Silene dichotoma
Italian	italica
Night-flowering	noctiflora
Nottingham	nutans
Sand	conica
Small-flowered	gallica
Spanish	otites
Sticky	Lychnis viscaria
Sweet-William	Silene armeria
Cat-mint	Nepeta cataria
Cat's-ear	Hypochoeris radicata
Smooth	glabra
Spotted	maculata
Cat's-tail, Alpine	Phleum alpinum
Purple-stem	phleoides
Sand	arenarium
Smaller	pratense subsp. bertolonii
Celandine, Greater	Chelidonium majus
Lesser	Ranunculus ficaria
Celery, Wild	Apium graveolens
Centaury, Broad-leaved	Centaurium latifolium
Common	erythraea
Guernsey	Exaculum pusillum
Lesser	Centaurium pulchellum
Perennial	scilloides

Centaury, Seaside

Centaury - contunued
   Seaside   Centaurium littorale
   Slender   tenuiflorum
   Tufted   capitatum
   Yellow   Cicendia filiformis

Chaffweed   Anagalis minima

Chamomile   Chamaemelum nobile
   Corn   Anthemis arvensis
   Stinking   cotula
   Yellow   tinctoria

Charlock   Sinapis arvensis

Cherry, Bird   Prunus padus
   Dwarf   cerasus
   Wild   avium

Chervil, Bur   Anthriscus caucalis
   Garden   cerefolium
   Golden   Chaerophyllum aureum
   Rough   temulentum

Chestnut see also Horse-c.
Chestnut, Sweet   Castanea sativa

Chickweed, Common   Stellaria media
   Greater   neglecta
   Lesser   pallida
   Upright   Moenchia erecta
   Water   Myosoton aquaticum

Chicory   Cichorium intybus

Chives   Allium schoenoprasum

Cicely, Sweet   Myrrhis odorata

Cinquefoil, Alpine   Potentilla crantzii
   Creeping   reptans
   Hoary   argentea
   Marsh   palustris
   Rock   rupestris
   Shrubby   fruticosa
   Spring   tabernaemontani
   Sulphur   recta
   Ternate-leaved   norvegica

Clary, Meadow   Salvia pratensis
   Whorled   verticillata
   Wild   verbenaca

Cleavers   Galium aparine
   Corn   tricornutum
   False   spurium

Cloudberry	Rubus chamaemorus
Clover, Alsike	Trifolium hybridum
Bird's-foot	ornithopodioides
Clustered	glomeratum
Crimson	incarnatum subsp. incarnatum
Hare's-foot	arvense
Knotted	striatum
Long-headed	incarnatum subsp. molineri
Red	pratense
Reversed	resupinatum
Rough	scabrum
Sea	squamosum
Starry	stellatum
Strawberry	fragiferum
Subterranean	subterraneum
Suffocated	suffocatum
Sulphur	ochroleucon
Twin-headed	bocconei
Upright	strictum
Western	occidentale
White	repens
Zigzag	medium
Clubmoss see also Alpine-c.	
Clubmoss, Fir	Huperzia selago
Interrupted	Lycopodium annotinum
Krauss's	Selaginella kraussiana
Lesser	selaginoides
Marsh	Lycopodiella inundatum
Stag's-horn	Lycopodium clavatum
Club-rush, Bristle	Isolepis setacea
Common	Schoenoplectus lacustris
Floating	Eleogiton fluitans
Grey	Schoenoplectus tabernaemontani
Round-headed	Holoschoenus vulgaris
Sea	Scirpus maritimus
Sharp	Schoenoplectus pungens
Slender	Isolepis cernua
Triangular	Schoenoplectus triqueter
Wood	Scirpus sylvaticus
Cocklebur, Rough	Xanthium strumarium
Spiny	spinosum
Cock's-eggs	Salpichroa origanifolia
Cock's-foot	Dactylis glomerata
Cockspur	Echinochloa crus-galli
Colt's-foot	Tussilago farfara
Purple	Homogyne alpina
Columbine	Aquilegia vulgaris

Columbine, Pyrenean

Columbine - continued
  Pyrenean   Aquilegia pyrenaica

Comfrey, Bulbous   Symphytum bulbosum
  Common   officinale
  Creeping   ibericum
  Crimean   tauricum
  Rough   asperum
  Russian   x uplandicum
  Tuberous   tuberosum
  White   orientale

Coneflower   Rudbeckia laciniata

Copse-bindweed   Fallopia dumetorum

Coral-necklace   Illecebrum verticillatum

Coralroot   Cardamine bulbifera

Cord-grass, Common   Spartima anglica
  Small   maritima
  Smooth   alterniflora
  Townsend's   x townsendii

Coriander   Coriandrum sativum

Corncockle   Agrostemma githago

Cornel, Dwarf   Cornus suecica

Cornflower   Centaurea cyanus
  Perennial   montana

Cornsalad, Broad-fruited Valerianella rimosa
  Common   locusta
  Hairy-fruited   eriocarpa
  Keeled-fruited   carinata
  Narrow-fruited   dentata

Corydalis, Climbing   Corydalis claviculata
  Yellow   lutea

Cotoneaster, Himalayan Cotoneaster simonsii
  Small-leaved   microphyllus
  Wall   horizontalis
  Wild   integerrimus

Cottongrass, Broad-leaved Eriophorum latifolium
  Common   angustifolium
  Hare's-tail   vaginatum
  Slender   gracile

Cottonweed   Otanthus maritimus

Couch, Bearded   Elymus caninus

74

Couch – <u>continued</u>
  Common   Elymus repens
  Sand   farctus
  Sea   pycnanthus

Cowbane   Cicuta virosa

Cowberry   Vaccinium vitis-idaea

Cowherb   Vaccaria hispanica

Cowslip   Primula veris

Cow-wheat, Common   Melampyrum pratense
  Crested   cristatum
  Field   arvense
  Small   sylvaticum

Cranberry   Vaccinium oxycoccus
  American   macrocarpum
  Small   microcarpum

Crane's-bill, Bloody   Geranium sanguineum
  Cut-leaved   dissectum
  Dove's-foot   molle
  Dusky   phaeum
  French   endressii
  Hedgerow   pyrenaicum
  Knotted   nodosum
  Long-stalked   columbinum
  Meadow   pratense
  Pencilled   versicolor
  Round-leaved   rotundifolium
  Shining   lucidum
  Small-flowered   pusillum
  Wood   sylvaticum

Creeping-Jenny   Lysimachia nummularia

Cress <u>see</u> <u>also</u> Bitter-c.,
    Penny-c., Rock-c.,
    Swine-c., Water-c.,
    Winter-c., Yellow-c.
Cress, Garden   Lepidium sativum
  Hoary   Cardaria draba
  Shepherd's   Teesdalia nudicaulis
  Thale   Arabidopsis thaliana
  Tower   Arabis turrita

Crocus, Autumn   Crocus nudiflorus
  Saffron   sativus
  Sand   Romulea columnae
  Spring   Crocus vernus subsp. vernus

Crosswort   Galium cruciata

Crowberry	Empetrum nigrum subsp. nigrum
Mountain	nigrum subsp. hermaphroditum

Crowfoot <u>see also</u> Water-c.

Crowfoot, Ivy-leaved	Ranunculus hederaceus
Round-leaved	omiophyllus
Three-lobed	tripartitus

Cuckooflower	Cardamine pratensis

Cudweed, Broad-leaved	Filago pyramidata
Common	vulgaris
Dwarf	Gnaphalium supinum
Heath	sylvaticum
Highland	norvegicum
Jersey	luteo-album
Marsh	uliginosum
Narrow-leaved	Filago gallica
Red-tipped	lutescens
Small	minima

Currant, Black	Ribes nigrum
Downy	spicatum
Flowering	sanguineum
Mountain	alpinum
Red	rubrum

Cut-grass	Leersia oryzoides

Cyclamen	Cyclamen hederifolium

Cyphel	Minuartia sedoides

Daffodil, Bunch-flowered	Narcissus tazetta
Pheasant's-eye	poeticus
Spanish	hispanicus
,Tenby	obvallaris
Wild	pseudonarcissus

Daisy <u>see also</u>
    Michaelmas-d.

Daisy	Bellis perennis
Oxeye	Leucanthemum vulgare
Shasta	maximum

Dame's-violet	Hesperis matronalis

Dandelion <u>see also</u> Marsh-d.

Dandelion, Common	Taraxacum officinale[*]
Lesser	laevigatum[*]

---

[*] Dandelions are now the subject of much study. If a correct
identification has been made it should be so indicated.

Dandelion - <u>continued</u>
  Red-veined   Taraxacum spectabile

Darnel   Lolium temulentum

Dead-nettle, Cut-leaved   Lamium hybridum
  Henbit   amplexicaule
  Northern   moluccellifolium
  Red   purpureum
  Spotted   maculatum
  White   album

Deergrass   Trichophorum cespitosum

Dewberry   Rubus caesius

Dew-plant, Deltoid-leaved Lampranthus deltoides
  Pale   Drosanthemum floribundum
  Purple   Disphyma crassifolium
  Rosy   Lampranthus roseus
  Sickle-leaved   falciformis

Diapensia   Diapensia lapponica

Dittander   Lepidium latifolium

Dock, Argentine   Rumex frutescens
  Blood-veined   sanguineus var. sanguineus
  Broad-leaved   obtusifolius
  Clustered   conglomeratus
  Curled   crispus
  Fiddle   pulcher
  Golden   maritimus
  Greek   cristatus
  Hooked   brownii
  Marsh   palustris
  Northern   longifolius
  Obovate-leaved   obovatus
  Patience   patientia
  Scottish   aquaticus
  Shore   rupestris
  Water   hydrolapathum
  Willow-leaved   triangulivalvis
  Wood   sanguineus var. viridis

Dodder   Cuscuta epithymum
  Flax   epilinum
  Greater   europaea

Dog-rose   Rosa canina
  Glaucous   afzeliana
  Hairy   coriifolia
  Round-leaved   obtusifolia
  Thicket   dumetorum

<u>Dog's-tail</u>, <u>Crested</u>

Dog's-tail, Crested	Cynosurus cristatus
Rough	echinatus
Dog-violet, Common	Viola riviniana
Early	reichenbachiana
Heath	canina
Pale	lactea
Dogwood	Cornus sanguinea
Red-Osier	sericea
Downy-rose, Harsh	Rosa tomentosa
Sherard's	sherardii
Soft	mollis
Dragon's-teeth	Tetragonolobus maritimus
Dropwort <u>see</u> <u>also</u> Water-d.	
Dropwort	Filipendula vulgaris
Duckweed, Common	Lemna minor
Fat	gibba
Greater	polyrhiza
Ivy-leaved	trisulca
Least	minuscula
Rootless	Wolffia arrhiza

Eelgrass	Zostera marina
Dwarf	noltii
Narrow-leaved	angustifolia
Elder <u>see</u> <u>also</u> Ground-e.	
Elder	Sambucus nigra
Dwarf	ebulus
Red-berried	racemosa
Elecampane	Inula helenium
Elm, English	Ulmus procera
Small-leaved	minor*
Wych	glabra
Enchanter's-nightshade	Circaea lutetiana
Alpine	alpina
Upland	x intermedia
Eryngo, Field	Eryngium campestre
Escallonia	Escallonia macrantha

* There are closely allied species which, if correctly identified, should be so indicated.

Evening-primrose, Common   Oenothera biennis
   Fragrant   stricta
   Large-flowered   erythrosepala
   Small-flowered   cambrica

Everlasting, Mountain   Antennaria dioica
   Pearly   Anaphalis margaritacea

Everlasting-pea, Broad-leaved   Lathyrus latifolius
   Narrow-leaved   sylvestris

Eyebright   Euphrasia officinalis[*]
   Irish   salisburgensis

False-acacia   Robinia pseudacacia

Fat-hen   Chenopodium album

Fennel   Foeniculum vulgare
   Hog's   Peucedanum officinale

Fen-sedge, Great   Cladium mariscus

Fern see also Bladder-f.,
   Buckler-f., Filmy-f.,
   Lady-f., Male-f.,
   Shield-f.
Fern, Beech   Phegopteris connectilis
   Hard   Blechnum spicant
   Holly   Polystichum lonchites
   Jersey   Anogramma leptophylla
   Killarney   Trichomanes speciosum
   Lemon-scented   Oreopteris limbosperma
   Limestone   Gymnocarpium robertianum
   Maidenhair   Adiantum capillus-veneris
   Marsh   Thelypteris palustris
   Oak   Gymnocarpium dryopteris
   Ostrich   Matteuccia struthiopteris
   Parsley   Cryptogramma crispa
   Royal   Osmunda regalis
   Sensitive   Onoclea sensibilis
   Water   Azolla filiculoides

Fern-grass   Desmazeria rigida
   Sea   marina

Fescue see also Sheep's-f.
Fescue, Bearded   Vulpia ciliata subsp. ambigua
   Blue   Festuca longifolia
   Breton   armoricana

[*] There are many microspecies which, if correctly identified, should
be so indicated.

Fescue - continued
  Chewings   Festuca nigrescens
  Dune   Vulpia fasciculata
  Foxtail   Vulpia megalura
  Giant   Festuca gigantea
  Hard   trachyphylla
  Hybrid   x Festulolium loliaceum
  Mat-grass   Vulpia unilateralis
  Meadow   Festuca pratensis
  Rat's-tail   Vulpia myuros
  Red   Festuca rubra
  Rush-leaved   juncifolia
  Squirreltail   Vulpia bromoides
  Tall   Festuca arundinacea
  Various-leaved   heterophylla
  Viviparous   vivipara
  Wood   altissima

Feverfew   Tanacetum parthenium

Fiddleneck   Amsinckia lycopsoides

Field-rose   Rosa arvensis
  Short-styled   stylosa

Field-speedwell, Common   Veronica persica
  Green   agrestis
  Grey   polita

Fig see also Hottentot-f.
Fig   Ficus carica

Figwort, Balm-leaved   Scrophularia scorodonia
  Common   nodosa
  Green   umbrosa
  Water   auriculata
  Yellow   vernalis

Filmy-fern, Tonbridge   Hymenophyllum tunbrigense
  Wilson's   wilsonii

Finger-grass, Hairy   Digitaria sanguinalis
  Smooth   ischaemum

Fir, Douglas   Pseudotsuga menziesii

Flag see Sweet-f.

Flat-Sedge   Blysmus compressus
  Saltmarsh   rufus

Flax see also New Zealand-f.
Flax   Linum usitatissimum
  Fairy   catharticum
  Pale   bienne
  Perennial   perenne subsp. anglicum

Fleabane, Alpine	Erigeron borealis
Argentine	Erigeron bonariensis
Blue	acer
Canadian	canadensis
Common	Pulicaria dysenterica
Irish	Inula salicina
Mexican	Erigeron mucronatus
Small	Pulicaria vulgaris
Fleawort, Field	Senecio integrifolius
Marsh	palustris
Flixweed	Descurainia sophia
Flowering-rush	Butomus umbellatus
Fluellen, Round-leaved	Kickxia spuria
Sharp-leaved	elatine
Forget-me-not, Alpine	Myosotis alpestris
Changing	discolor
Creeping	secunda
Early	ramosissima
Field	arvensis
Jersey	sicula
Pale	stolonifera
Tufted	laxa subsp. caespitosa
Water	scorpioides
Wood	sylvatica
Fox-and-cubs	Hieracium aurantiacum
Foxglove	Digitalis purpurea
Fairy	Erinus alpinus
Fox-sedge, False	Carex otrubae
True	vulpina
Foxtail, Alpine	Alopecurus alpinus
Bulbous	bulbosus
Marsh	geniculatus
Meadow	pratensis
Orange	aequalis
Fringe-cups	Tellima grandiflora
Fritillary	Fritillaria meleagris
Frogbit	Hydrocharis morsus-ranae
Fuchsia	Fuchsia magellanica
Fumitory see also Ramping-f.	
Fumitory, Common	Fumaria officinalis
Dense-flowered	densiflora
Few-flowered	vaillantii

Fumitory - continued
  Fine-leaved   Fumaria parviflora

Galingale   Cyperus longus
  Brown   fuscus

Garlic, Field   Allium oleraceum
  Keeled   carinatum
  Rosy   roseum

Gentian, Alpine   Gentiana nivalis
  Autumn   Gentianella amarella
  Chiltern   germanica
  Dune   uliginosa
  Early   anglica
  Field   campestris
  Marsh   Gentiana pneumonanthe
  Spring   verna

Germander, Cut-leaved   Teucrium botrys
  Wall   chamaedrys
  Water   scordium

Giant-rhubarb   Gunnera tinctoria
  Brazilian   manicata

Gipsywort   Lycopus europaeus

Gladiolus, Wild   Gladiolus illyricus

Glasswort   Salicornia europaea*
  Perennial   perennis

Globeflower   Trollius europaeus

Goat's-beard   Tragopogon pratensis

Goat's-rue   Galega officinalis

Goldenrod   Solidago virgaurea
  Canadian   canadensis
  Early   gigantea

Golden-samphire   Inula crithmoides

Golden-saxifrage, Alternate-leaved   Chrysosplenium alternifolium
  Opposite-leaved   oppositifolium

Gold-of-pleasure   Camelina sativa

* There are closely allied species which, if correctly identified,
  should be so indicated.

Good-King-Henry	Chenopodium bonus-henricus
Gooseberry	Ribes uva-crispa
Goosefoot, Fig-leaved	Chenopodium ficifolium
Grey	opulifolium
Many-seeded	polyspermum
Maple-leaved	hybridum
Nettle-leaved	murale
Oak-leaved	glaucum
Red	rubrum
Saltmarsh	botryodes
Stinking	vulvaria
Upright	urbicum
Gorse	Ulex europaeus
Dwarf	minor
Western	gallii
Grape see also Oregon-g.	
Grape-vine	Vitis vinifera
Grass see Introduction for treatment of grasses	
Grass-of-Parnassus	Parnassia palustris
Grass-poly	Lythrum hyssopifolia
Greenweed, Dyer's	Genista tinctoria
Hairy	pilosa
Gromwell, Common	Lithospermum officinale
Field	arvense
Purple	purpurocaeruleum
Ground-elder	Aegopodium podagraria
Ground-ivy	Glechoma hederacea
Ground-pine	Ajuga chamaepitys
Groundsel	Senecio vulgaris
Heath	sylvaticus
Sticky	viscosus
Welsh	cambrensis
Guelder-rose	Viburnum opulus
Hair-grass, Alpine	Deschampsia alpina
Bog	setacea
Crested	Koeleria macrantha

Hair-grass, <u>Dune</u>

Hair-grass - <u>continued</u>
  Dune   Koeleria glauca
  Early   Aira praecox
  Grey   Corynephorus canescens
  Silver   Aira caryophyllea
  Somerset   Koeleria vallesiana
  Tufted   Deschampsia cespitosa
  Wavy   flexuosa

Hairy-brome   Bromus ramosus
  Lesser   benekenii

Hampshire-purslane   Ludwigia palustris

Hard-grass   Parapholis strigosa
  Curved   incurva

Harebell   Campanula rotundifolia

Hare's-ear, Shrubby Bupleurum fruticosum
  Sickle-leaved   falcatum
  Slender   tenuissimum
  Small   baldense

Hare's-tail   Lagurus ovatus

Hart's-tongue   Phyllitis scolopendrium

Hartwort   Tordylium maximum

Hawkbit, Autumn   Leontodon autumnalis
  Lesser   taraxacoides
  Rough   hispidus

Hawk's-beard, Beaked Crepis vesicaria subsp.
                    haenseleri
  Bristly   setosa
  Marsh   paludosa
  Narrow-leaved   tectorum
  Northern   mollis
  Rough   biennis
  Smooth   capillaris
  Stinking   foetida

Hawkweed, Common   Hieracium vulgatum[*]
  Mouse-ear   pilosella
  Spotted   maculatum

Hawthorn   Crataegus monogyna
  Midland   laevigata

Hazel   Corylus avellana

[*] There are numerous microspecies which, if correctly identified, should be so indicated.

Heath <u>see</u> <u>also</u> Sea-h.

Heath, Blue	Phyllodoce caerulea
Cornish	Erica vagans
Corsican	terminalis
Cross-leaved	tetralix
Dorset	ciliaris
Irish	erigena
Mackay's	mackaiana
Prickly	Pernettya mucronata
St Dabeoc's	Daboecia cantabrica
Heather	Calluna vulgaris
Bell	Erica cinerea
Heath-grass	Danthonia decumbens
Hedge-bedstraw	Galium mollugo
Upright	album
Hedge-parsley, Knotted	Torilis nodosa
Spreading	arvensis
Upright	japonica
Heliotrope, Winter	Petasites fragrans
Hellebore, Green	Helleborus viridus
Stinking	foetidus
Helleborine, Broad-leaved	Epipactis helleborine
Dark-red	atrorubens
Dune	dunensis
Green-flowered	phyllanthes
Marsh	palustris
Narrow-leaved	Cephalanthera longifolia
Narrow-lipped	Epipactis leptochila
Red	Cephalanthera rubra
Violet	Epipactis purpurata
White	Cephalanthera damasonium
Hemlock	Conium maculatum
Hemlock-spruce, Western	Tsuga heterophylla
Hemp	Cannabis sativa
Hemp-agrimony	Eupatorium cannabinum
Hemp-nettle, Broad-leaved	Galeopsis ladanum
Common	tetrahit
Downy	segetum
Large-flowered	speciosa
Lesser	bifida
Red	angustifolia
Henbane	Hyoscyamus niger

Herb-Paris

Herb-Paris	Paris quadrifolia
Herb-Robert	Geranium robertianum
Hogweed	Heracleum sphondylium
Giant	mantegazzianum

Holly **see** **also** Sea-h.

Holly	Ilex aquifolium
Hollyhock	Alcea rosea
Holy-grass	Hierochloe odorata
Honesty	Lunaria annua
Honewort	Trinia glauca
Honeysuckle	Lonicera periclymenum
Fly	xylosteum
Himalayan	Leycesteria formosa
Perfoliate	Lonicera caprifolium
Hop	Humulus lupulus
Horehound, Black	Ballota nigra
White	Marrubium vulgare
Hornbeam	Carpinus betulus
Horned-poppy, Violet	Roemeria hybrida
Yellow	Glaucium flavum
Hornwort, Rigid	Ceratophyllum demersum
Soft	submersum
Horse-chestnut	Aesculus hippocastanum
Horse-radish	Armoracia rusticana
Horsetail, Field	Equisetum arvense
Great	telmateia
Marsh	palustre
Rough	hyemale
Shady	pratense
Variegated	variegatum
Water	fluviatile
Wood	sylvaticum
Hottentot-fig	Carpobrotus edulis var. edulis
Hound's-tongue	Cynoglossum officinale
Green	germanicum
House-leek	Sempervivum tectorum

Hutchinsia	Hornungia petraea
Hyacinth, Grape	Muscari neglectum
Hydrilla	Hydrilla verticillata
Hyssop	Hyssopus officinalis

Iceland-purslane	Koenigia islandica
Iris, Blue	Iris spuria
Flag	germanica
Purple	versicolor
Snake's-head	Hermodactylus tuberosus
Stinking	Iris foetidissima
Yellow	pseudacorus

Ivy see also Ground-i.

Ivy	Hedera helix
Irish	hibernica

Jacob's-ladder	Polemonium caeruleum
Japanese-lantern	Physalis alkekengi
Jonquil	Narcissus jonquilla
Juneberry	Amelanchier lamarckii
Juniper	Juniperus communis

Kale see Sea-k.

Karo	Pittosporum crassifolium
Knapweed, Brown	Centaurea jacea
Common	nigra
Greater	scabiosa
Jersey	paniculata
Slender	nemoralis
Knawel, Annual	Scleranthus annuus
Perennial	perennis
Knotgrass	Polygonum aviculare
Cornfield	rurivagum
Equal-leaved	arenastrum

Knotgrass - continued
Northern	Polygonum boreale
Ray's	oxyspermum subsp. raii
Sea	maritimum

Knotweed, Alpine	Polygonum alpinum
Giant	Reynoutria sachalinense
Himalayan	Polygonum polystachyum
Japanese	Reynoutria japonica
Lesser	Polygonum campanulatum

Koromiko	Hebe salicifolia
Labrador-tea	Ledum palustre
Laburnum	Laburnum anagyroides

Lady-fern	Athyrium filix-femina
Alpine	distentifolium

Lady's-mantle	Alchemilla vulgaris agg.*
Alpine	alpina
Hairy	filicaulis
Intermediate	xanthochlora
Smooth	glabra

Lady's-slipper	Cypripedium calceolus

Lady's-tresses, Autumn	Spiranthes spiralis
Creeping	Goodyera repens
Irish	Spiranthes romanzoffiana
Summer	aestivalis

Larch, European	Larix decidua
Japanese	kaempferi

Larkspur	Consolida ambigua

Laurel see also Spurge-1.
Laurel, Cherry	Prunus laurocerasus
Portugal	lusitanica

Laurustinus	Viburnum tinus

Lavender see Sea-1.

Leek see also House-1.
Leek, Babington's	Allium ampeloprasum subsp.
	babingtonii
Few-flowered	paradoxum
Round-headed	sphaerocephalon
Sand	scorodoprasum

* There are a number of microspecies which, if correctly identified, should be so indicated.

Leek - continued
Three-cornered   Allium triquetrum
Wild   ampeloprasum subsp.
                                ampeloprasum

Leopard's-bane   Doronicum pardalianches
Plantain-leaved   plantagineum

Lettuce, Garden   Lactuca sativa
Great   virosa
Least   saligna
Prickly   serriola
Wall   Mycelis muralis

Lilac   Syringa vulgaris

Lily see also Water-l.
Lily, Kerry   Simethis planifolia
Martagon   Lilium martagon
May   Maianthemum bifolium
Pyrenean   Lilium pyrenaicum
Snowdon   Lloydia serotina

Lily-of-the-valley   Convallaria majalis

Lime   Tilia x vulgaris
Large-leaved   platyphyllos
Small-leaved   cordata

Liquorice, Wild   Astragalus glycphyllos

Little-Robin   Geranium purpureum

Lobelia, Heath   Lobelia urens
Water   dortmanna

Londonpride   Saxifraga x urbium

London-rocket   Sisymbrium irio
False   loeselii

Longleaf   Falcaria vulgaris

Loosestrife, see also Purple-l.
Loosestrife, Dotted   Lysimachia punctata
Fringed   ciliata
Lake   terrestris
Tufted   thyrsiflora
Yellow   vulgaris

Lords-and-Ladies   Arum maculatum
Italian   italicum

Lousewort   Pedicularis sylvatica
Marsh   palustris

Lovage, Scots	Ligusticum scoticum
Lucerne	Medicago sativa

Lungwort
   Narrow-leaved
	Pulmonaria officinalis
	   longifolia

Lupin, Garden
   Nootka
   Tree
	Lupinus polyphyllus
	   nootkatensis
	   arboreus

Lyme-grass	Leymus arenarius
Madder, Field Wild	Sherardia arvensis Rubia peregrina
Madwort	Asperugo procumbens

Male-fern
   Mountain
   Scaly
	Dryopteris filix-mas
	   oreades
	   affinis

Mallow <u>see also</u> Marsh-m., Tree-m.
Mallow, Chinese
   Common
   Dwarf
   Least
   Musk
   Small
	Malva verticillata
	   sylvestris
	   neglecta
	   parviflora
	   moschata
	   pusilla

Maple, Field
   Norway
	Acer campestre
	   platanoides

Mare's-tail	Hippuris vulgaris

Marigold <u>see also</u> Bur-m., Marsh-m.
Marigold, Corn
   Field
   Pot
	Chrysanthemum segetum
	Calendula arvensis
	   officinalis

Marjoram	Origanum vulgare
Marram Purple	Ammophila arenaria x Ammocalamagrostis baltica

Marsh-bedstraw, Common
   Great
   Slender
	Galium palustre
	   elongatum
	   debile

Marsh-dandelion, Narrow-leaved	Taraxacum palustre[*]

* Dandelions are now the subject of much study. If a correct identification has been made it should be so indicated.

Marsh-mallow	Althaea officinalis
Rough	hirsuta
Marsh-marigold	Caltha palustris
Marsh-orchid, Broad-leaved	Dactylorhiza majalis
Early	incarnata
Flecked	cruenta
Narrow-leaved	traunsteineri
Northern	purpurella
Southern	praetermissa
Marshwort, Creeping	Apium repens
Lesser	inundatum
Masterwort	Peucedanum ostruthium
Mat-grass	Nardus stricta
Mayweed, Scented	Matricaria recutita
Scentless	Tripleurospermum inodorum
Sea	maritimum
Meadow-grass, Alpine	Poa alpina
Annual	annua
Broad-leaved	chaixii
Bulbous	bulbosa
Early	infirma
Flattened	compressa
Glaucous	glauca
Narrow-leaved	angustifolia
Rough	trivialis
Smooth	pratensis
Spreading	subcaerulea
Swamp	palustris
Wavy	flexuosa
Wood	nemoralis
Meadow-rue, Alpine	Thalictrum alpinum
Common	flavum
Lesser	minus
Meadowsweet	Filipendula ulmaria
Medick, Black	Medicago lupulina
Bur	minima
Sickle	falcata
Spotted	arabica
Toothed	polymorpha
Medlar	Mespilus germanica
Melick, Mountain	Melica nutans
Wood	uniflora
Melilot, Ribbed	Melilotus officinalis

Melilot, Small

Melilot - continued	
Small	Melilotus indica
Tall	altissima
White	alba
Mercury, Annual	Mercurialis annua
Dog's	perennis
Mezereon	Daphne mezereum
Michaelmas-daisy	Aster novi-belgii[*]
Hairy	novi-angliae
Mignonette, White	Reseda alba
Wild	lutea
Milfoil see Water-m.	
Milk-parsley	Peucedanum palustre
Cambridge	Selinum carvifolia
Milk-vetch, Alpine	Astragalus alpinus
Purple	danicus
Milkwort see also Sea-m.	
Milkwort, Chalk	Polygala calcarea
Common	vulgaris
Dwarf	amarella
Heath	serpyllifolia
Millet, Common	Panicum miliaceum
Early	Milium vernale
Wood	effusum
Mind-your-own-business	Soleirolia soleirolii
Mint, Apple	Mentha x villosa
Corn	arvensis
Corsican	requienii
Round-leaved	suaveolens
Spear	spicata
Water	aquatica
Whorled	x verticillata
Mintweed	Salvia reflexa
Mistletoe	Viscum album
Moneywort, Cornish	Sibthorpia europaea
Monkeyflower	Mimulus guttatus

[*] This is probably the most common of a number of closely allied species. If a correct identification has been made this should be so indicated.

Monk's-hood	Aconitum napellus
Monk's-rhubarb	Rumex alpinus
Montbretia	Tritonia x crocosmiflora
Moonwort	Botrychium lunaria
Moor-grass, Blue	Sesleria albicans
Purple	Molinia caerulea
Moschatel	Adoxa moschatellina
Motherwort	Leonurus cardiaca
Mouse-ear, Alpine	Cerastium alpinum
Arctic	arcticum subsp. arcticum
Common	fontanum subsp. glabrescens
Dwarf	pumilum
Field	arvense
Grey	brachypetalum
Little	semidecandrum
Sea	diffusum
Shetland	arcticum subsp. edmondstonii
Starwort	cerastoides
Sticky	glomeratum
Mousetail	Myosurus minimus
Mudwort	Limosella aquatica
Welsh	australis
Mugwort	Artemisia vulgaris
Chinese	verlotorum
Hoary	stellerana
Norwegian	norvegica
Mullein, Dark	Verbascum nigrum
Great	thapsus
Hoary	pulverulentum
Moth	blattaria
Orange	phlomoides
Twiggy	virgatum
White	lychnitis
Musk	Mimulus moschatus
Mustard, Ball	Neslia paniculata
Black	Brassica nigra
Garlic	Alliaria petiolata
Hare's-ear	Conringia orientalis
Hedge	Sisymbrium officinale
Hoary	Hirschfeldia incana
Tower	Arabis glabra
Treacle	Erysimum cheiranthoides
White	Sinapis alba

Myrtle

Myrtle, see Bog-m.

Naiad, Holly-leaved	Najas marina
Slender	flexilis
Navelwort	Umbilicus rupestris

Nettle see also Dead-n., Hemp-n.

Nettle, Common	Urtica dioica
Roman	pilulifera
Small	urens
New Zealand-flax	Phormium tenax

Nightshade see also Enchanters-n.

Nightshade, Black	Solanum nigrum
Deadly	Atropa belladonna
Green	Solanum sarrachoides
Three-flowered	triflorum
Nipplewort	Lapsana communis
Nit-grass	Gastridium ventricosum

Oak, Evergreen	Quercus ilex
Pedunculate	robur
Red	borealis var. maxima
Sessile	petraea
Turkey	cerris

Oat see also Wild-o.

Oat	Avena sativa
Bristle	strigosa
Oat-grass, Downy	Avenula pubescens
False	Arrhenatherum elatius
Meadow	Avenula pratensis
Yellow	Trisetum flavescens
Onion, Wild	Allium vineale
Orache, Babington's	Atriplex glabriuscula
Common	patula
Early	praecox
Frosted	laciniata
Garden	hortensis
Grass-leaved	littoralis
Long-stalked	longipes
Shrubby	halimus
Spear-leaved	prostrata

Orchid see also Butterfly-o., Marsh-o., Spider-o., Spotted-o.	
Orchid, Bee	Ophrys apifera
Bird's-nest	Neottia nidus-avis
Bog	Hammarbya paludosa
Burnt	Orchis ustulata
Coralroot	Corallorhiza trifida
Dense-flowered	Neotinea maculata
Early-purple	Orchis mascula
Fen	Liparis loeselii
Fly	Ophrys insectifera
Fragrant	Gymnadenia conopsea
Frog	Coeloglossum viride
Ghost	Epipogium aphyllum
Green-winged	Orchis morio
Lady	purpurea
Lizard	Himantoglossum hircinum
Loose-flowered	Orchis laxiflora
Man	Aceras anthropophorum
Military	Orchis militaris
Monkey	simia
Musk	Herminium monorchis
Pyramidal	Anacamptis pyramidalis
Small-white	Pseudorchis albida
Oregon-grape	Mahonia aquifolium
Orpine	Sedum telephium
Osier	Salix viminalis
Oxlip	Primula elatior
False	veris x vulgaris
Oxtongue, Bristly	Picris echioides
Hawkweed	hieracioides
Oxytropis, Purple	Oxytropis halleri
Yellow	campestris
Oysterplant	Mertensia maritima
Pampas-grass	Cortaderia selloana
Pansy, Dwarf	Viola kitaibeliana
Field	arvensis
Mountain	lutea
Wild	tricolor
Parsley see also Bur-p., Hedge-p., Milk-p.	
Parsley, Corn	Petroselinum segetum
Cow	Anthriscus sylvestris

Parsley - continued
  Fool's   Aethusa cynapium
  Garden   Petroselinum crispum
  Stone   Sison amomum

Parsley-piert   Aphanes arvensis
  Slender   microcarpa

Parsnip see also Water-p.
Parsnip, Wild   Pastinaca sativa

Pasqueflower   Pulsatilla vulgaris

Pea see also Everlasting-p.
Pea, Black   Lathyrus niger
  Marsh   palustris
  Sea   japonicus
  Tuberous   tuberosus

Pear, Plymouth   Pyrus cordata
  Wild   pyraster

Pearlwort, Alpine   Sagina saginoides
  Annual   apetala
  Heath   subulata
  Knotted   nodosa
  Procumbent   procumbens
  Scottish   x normaniana
  Sea   maritima
  Snow   intermedia

Pellitory-of-the-wall Parietaria judaica

Penny-cress, Alpine Thlaspi alpestre
  Field   arvense
  Garlic   alliaceum
  Perfoliate   perfoliatum

Pennyroyal   Mentha pulegium

Pennywort, Hairy   Hydrocotyle moschata
  Marsh   vulgaris

Peony   Paeonia mascula

Pepper see Water-p.

Peppermint   Mentha x piperita

Pepper-saxifrage   Silaum silaus

Pepperwort, Field   Lepidium campestre
  Least   neglectum
  Narrow-leaved   ruderale
  Smith's   heterophyllum
  Tall   graminifolium

Periwinkle, Greater	Vinca major
Lesser	minor
Persicaria, Pale	Polygonum lapathifolium
Pheasant's-eye	Adonis annua
Pick-a-back-plant	Tolmiea menziesii
Pigmyweed	Crassula aquatica
Australian	helmsii
Pignut	Conopodium majus
Great	Bunium bulbocastanum
Pillwort	Pilularia globulifera
Pimpernel, Blue	Anagalis arvensis subsp.
	foemina
Bog	tenella
Scarlet	arvensis subsp. arvensis
Yellow	Lysimachia nemorum
Pine see also Ground-p.	
Pine, Austrian	Pinus nigra subsp. nigra
Corsican	nigra subsp. laricio
Maritime	pinaster
Monterey	radiata
Scots	sylvestris
Pineappleweed	Matricaria matricarioides
Pink	Dianthus plumarius
Cheddar	gratianopolitanus
Childing	Petrorhagia nanteuilii
Clove	Dianthus caryophyllus
Deptford	armeria
Jersey	gallicus
Maiden	deltoides
Proliferous	prolifera
Pink-sorrel	Oxalis articulata
Garden	latifolia
Large-flowered	corymbosa
Pale	incarnata
Pinkweed	Polygonum pensylvanicum
Pipewort	Eriocaulon aquaticum
Pirri-pirri-bur	Acaena novae-zelandiae
Pitcherplant	Sarracenia purpurea
Plane, London	Platanus x hybrida

Plantain, Branched

Plantain see also Water-p.
Plantain, Branched   Plantago arenaria
  Buck's-horn   coronopus
  Greater   major
  Hoary   media
  Ribwort   lanceolata
  Sea   maritima

Ploughman's-spikenard   Inula conyza

Plum, Cherry   Prunus cerasifera
  Wild   domestica

Polypody   Polypodium vulgare
  Intermediate   interjectum
  Southern   cambricum

Pond-sedge, Greater   Carex riparia
  Lesser   acutiformis

Pondweed, American   Potamogeton epihydrus
  Blunt-leaved   obtusifolius
  Bog   polygonifolius
  Broad-leaved   natans
  Curled   crispus
  Fen   coloratus
  Fennel   pectinatus
  Flat-stalked   friesii
  Grass-wrack   compressus
  Hairlike   trichoides
  Horned   Zannichellia palustris
  Lesser   Potamogeton pusillus
  Loddon   nodosus
  Long-stalked   praelongus
  Opposite-leaved   Groenlandia densa
  Perfoliate   Potamogeton perfoliatus
  Red   alpinus
  Sharp-leaved   acutifolius
  Shetland   rutilus
  Shining   lucens
  Slender-leaved   filiformis
  Small   berchtoldii
  Various-leaved   gramineus

Poplar see also Balm-of-Gilead,
    Balsam-p.
Poplar, Black   Populus nigra
  Grey   x canescens
  Italian   x canadensis var. serotina
  Lombardy   nigra var. italica
  White   alba

Poppy see also Horned-p.
Poppy, Atlas   Papaver atlanticum
  Californian   Eschscholzia californica
  Common   Papaver rhoeas

Poppy - <u>continued</u>
  Long-headed   Papaver dubium
  Opium   somniferum
  Prickly   argemone
  Rough   hybridum
  Welsh   Meconopsis cambrica
  Yellow-juiced   Papaver lecoqii

Prickly-sedge, Large-fruited   Carex muricata subsp. muricata
  Small-fruited   muricata subsp. lamprocarpa

Primrose <u>see</u> <u>also</u> Evening-p.
Primrose   Primula vulgaris
  Bird's-eye   farinosa
  Scottish   scotica

Primrose-peerless   Narcissus x medioluteus

Privet, Garden   Ligustrum ovalifolium
  Wild   vulgare

Purple-loosestrife   Lythrum salicaria

Purslane <u>see</u> <u>also</u>
    Hampshire-p., Iceland-p.,
    Sea-p., Water-p.
Purslane, Common   Portulaca oleracea
  Pink   Montia sibirica

Quaking-grass   Briza media
  Great   maxima
  Lesser   minor

Quillwort   Isoetes lacustris
  Land   histrix
  Spring   echinospora

Radish <u>see</u> <u>also</u> Horse-r
Radish, Garden   Raphanus sativus
  Sea   maritimus
  Wild   raphanistrum

Ragged-Robin   Lychnis flos-cuculi

Ragweed   Ambrosia artemisiifolia

Ragwort, Broad-leaved   Senecio fluviatilis
  Common   jacobaea
  Fen   paludosus
  Golden   doria

Ragwort, Hoary

Ragwort - continued
  Hoary   Senecio erucifolius
  Magellan   smithii
  Marsh   aquaticus
  Oxford   squalidus
  Silver   bicolor

Ramping-fumitory, Common   Fumaria muralis
  Martin's   martinii
  Purple   purpurea
  Tall   bastardii
  Western   occidentalis
  White   capreolata

Rampion, Round-headed   Phyteuma orbiculare
  Spiked   spicatum

Ramsons   Allium ursinum

Rannoch-rush   Scheuchzeria palustris

Rape   Brassica napus

Raspberry   Rubus idaeus

Rattle see Yellow-r.

Redshank   Polygonum persicaria

Reed see also Bur-r., Small-r.
Reed, Common   Phragmites australis

Restharrow, Common   Ononis repens
  Small   reclinata
  Spiny   spinosa

Rhododendron   Rhododendron ponticum

Rhubarb see also Giant-r.,
    Monk's-r.
Rhubarb   Rheum rhabarbarum

Robin see Ragged-r.

Rock-cress, Alpine   Arabis alpina
  Bristol   stricta
  Fringed   brownii
  Hairy   hirsuta
  Northern   Cardaminopsis petraea

Rocket see also London-r., Wall-r.
Rocket, Eastern   Sisymbrium orientale
  Garden   Eruca vesicaria subsp. sativa
  Hairy   Erucastrum gallicum
  Perennial   Sisymbrium strictissimum
  Sea   Cakile maritima
  Tall   Sisymbrium altissimum
100

Rocket - continued
 White   Diplotaxis erucoides

Rock-rose, Common   Helianthemum nummularium
 Hoary   canum
 Spotted   Tuberaria guttata
 White   Helianthemum apenninum

Rose see also Dog-r.,
    Downy-r., Field-r.,
    Guelder-r., Rock-r.
Rose, Burnet   Rosa pimpinellifolia
 Japanese   rugosa
 Many-flowered   multiflora
 Virginian   virginiana

Rose-of-Sharon   Hypericum calycinum

Rosemary see Bog-r.

Roseroot   Sedum rosea

Rowan   Sorbus aucuparia

Rue see Goat's-r.,
    Meadow-r., Wall-r.

Rupturewort, Fringed   Herniaria ciliolata
 Hairy   hirsuta
 Smooth   glabra

Rush see also Bog-r.,
    Club-r., Flowering-r.,
    Rannoch-r., Soft-r.,
    Spike-r., Wood-r.
Rush, Alpine   Juncus alpinus
 Baltic   balticus
 Blunt-flowered   subnodulosus
 Broad-leaved   planifolius
 Bulbous   bulbosus
 Chestnut   castaneus
 Compact   conglomeratus
 Diffuse   x diffusus
 Dudley's   dudleyi
 Dwarf   capitatus
 Hard   inflexus
 Heath   squarrosus
 Jointed   articulatus
 Marshall's   nodulosus
 Pigmy   pygmaeus
 Round-fruited   compressus
 Saltmarsh   gerardi
 Sea   maritimus
 Sharp   acutus
 Sharp-flowered   acutiflorus
 Slender   tenuis

Rush - continued
Thread	Juncus filiformis
Three-flowered	triglumis
Three-leaved	trifidus
Toad	bufonius
Two-flowered	biglumis

Russian-vine	Fallopia aubertii
Rustyback	Ceterach officinarum
Rye-grass, Italian	Lolium perenne subsp. multiflorum
perennial	perenne subsp. perenne

Saffron, Meadow	Colchicum autumnale
Sage, Jerusalem	Phlomis fruticosa
Wood	Teucrium scorodonia
Sainfoin	Onobrychis viciifolia

St John's-wort
Hairy	hirsutum
Imperforate	maculatum
Irish	canadense
Marsh	elodes
Pale	montanum
Perforate	perforatum
Slender	pulchrum
Square-stalked	tetrapterum
Toadflax-leaved	linarifolium
Trailing	humifusum
Wavy	undulatum

St Patrick's-cabbage	Saxifraga spathularis
Sally-my-handsome	Carprobrotus edulis var. rubescens
Salmonberry	Rubus spectabilis
Salsify	Tragopogon porrifolius

Saltmarsh-grass, Borrer's
	Puccinellia fasciculata
Common	maritima
Greater	pseudodistans
Northern	distans subsp. borealis
Reflexed	distans subsp. distans
Stiff	rupestris

Saltwort, Prickly
	Salsola kali subsp. kali
Spineless	kali subsp. ruthenica

Samphire, Rock	Crithmum maritimum
Sand-grass, Early	Mibora minima
Sandwort, Arctic	Arenaria norvegica subsp. norvegica
English	norvegica subsp. anglica
Fine-leaved	Minuartia hybrida
Fringed	Arenaria ciliata subsp. hibernica
Mossy	balearica
Mountain	Minuartia rubella
Recurved	recurva
Sea	Honkenya peploides
Slender	Arenaria leptoclados
Spring	Minuartia verna
Teesdale	stricta
Three-nerved	Moehringia trinervia
Thyme-leaved	Arenaria serpyllifolia
Sanicle	Sanicula europaea
Savory, Winter	Satureja montana
Saw-wort	Serratula tinctoria
Alpine	Saussurea alpina
Saxifrage see also Burnet-s., Golden-s., Pepper-s.	
Saxifrage, Alpine	Saxifraga nivalis
Celandine	cymbalaria
Drooping	cernua
Highland	rivularis
Irish	rosacea
Kidney	hirsuta
Marsh	hirculus
Meadow	granulata
Mossy	hypnoides
Purple	oppositifolia
Pyrenean	umbrosa
Rue-leaved	tridactylites
Starry	stellaris
Tufted	cespitosa
Yellow	aizoides
Scabious, Devils'-bit	Succisa pratensis
Field	Knautia arvensis
Small	Scabiosa columbaria
Scurvygrass, Alpine	Cochlearia alpina
Atlantic	atlantica
Common	officinalis
Danish	danica
English	anglica
Iceland	islandica
Mountain	micacea

103

Scurvygrass, Pyrenean

Scurvygrass - continued
  Pyrenean   Cochlearis pyrenaica
  Scottish   scotica

Sea-blite, Annual   Suaeda maritima
  Shrubby   vera

Sea-buckthorn   Hippophae rhamnoides

Sea-heath   Frankenia laevis

Sea-holly   Eryngium maritimum

Sea-kale   Crambe maritima

Seal see Solomon's-s.

Sea-lavender, Alderney   Limonium normannicum
  Common   vulgare
  Jersey   auriculae-ursifolium
  Lax-flowered   humile
  Matted   bellidifolium
  Rock   binervosum

Sea-milkwort   Glaux maritima

Sea-purslane   Halimione portulacoides

Sea-spurrey, Greater   Spergularia media
  Greek   bocconii
  Lesser   marina
  Rock   rupicola

Sedge see also Alpine-s., Beak-s.,
    Bladder-s., Bog-s., Fen-s.,
    Flat-s., Fox-s., Pond-s.,
    Prickly-s., Spring-s.,
    Tufted-s., Tussock-s.,
    Wood-s., Yellow-s.
Sedge, Bird's-foot   Carex ornithopoda
  Bottle   rostrata
  Bristle   microglochin
  Brown   disticha
  Carnation   panicea
  Club   buxbaumii
  Common   nigra
  Curved   maritima
  Cyperus   pseudocyperus
  Dioecious   dioica
  Distant   distans
  Divided   divisa
  Dotted   punctata
  Downy-fruited   tomentosa
  Dwarf   humilis
  Elongated   elongata

Sedge - continued

Estuarine	Carex recta
False	Kobresia simpliciuscula
Few-flowered	Carex pauciflora
Fingered	digitata
Flea	pulicaris
Glaucous	flacca
Green-ribbed	binervis
Grey	divulsa
Hair	capillaris
Hairy	hirta
Hare's-foot	lachenalii
Long-bracted	extensa
Oval	ovalis
Pale	pallescens
Pendulous	pendula
Pill	pilulifera
Remote	remota
Rock	rupestris
Russet	saxatilis
Sand	arenaria
Sheathed	vaginata
Slender	lasiocarpa
Smooth-stalked	laevigata
Soft-leaved	montana
Spiked	spicata
Star	echinata
Stiff	bigelowii
String	chordorrhiza
Tawny	hostiana
Water	aquatilis
White	curta
Selfheal	Prunella vulgaris
Cut-leaved	laciniata
Service-tree	Sorbus domestica
Wild	torminalis
Shallon	Gaultheria shallon
Sheep's-bit	Jasione montana
Sheep's-fescue	Festuca ovina
Fine-leaved	tenuifolia
Shepherd's-needle	Scandix pecten-veneris
Shepherd's-purse	Capsella bursa-pastoris
Shield-fern, Hard	Polystichum aculeatum
Soft	setiferum
Shoreweed	Littorella uniflora
Sibbaldia	Sibbaldia procumbens

Silky-bent, Dense	Apera interrupta
Loose	spica-venti
Silverweed	Potentilla anserina
Skullcap	Scutellaria galericulata
Lesser	minor
Norfolk	hastifolia
Small-reed, Narrow	Calamagrostis stricta
Purple	canescens
Scottish	scotica
Wood	epigejos
Snapdragon	Antirrhinum majus
Lesser	Misopates orontium
Sneezewort	Achillea ptarmica
Snowberry	Symphoricarpos rivularis
Snowdrop	Galanthus nivalis
Snowflake, Spring	Leucojum vernum
Summer	aestivum
Snow-in-summer	Cerastium tomentosum
Soapwort	Saponaria officinalis
Soft-brome	Bromus hordeaceus subsp. hordeaceus
Least	hordeaceus subsp. ferronii
Lesser	x pseudothominii
Slender	lepidus
Soft-grass, Creeping	Holcus mollis
Soft-rush	Juncus effusus
Great	pallidus
Soldier see also Water-s.	
Soldier, Gallant	Galinsoga parviflora
Shaggy	ciliata
Solomon's-seal	Polygonatum multiflorum
Angular	odoratum
Whorled	verticillatum
Sorrel see also Pink-s., Wood-s., Yellow-s.	
Sorrel, Common	Rumex acetosa
French	scutatus
Garden	rugosus
Irish	hibernicus
Mountain	Oxyria digyna
Narrow-leaved	Rumex tenuifolius

Sorrel - continued
  Sheep's   Rumex acetosella

Sow-thistle see also Blue-s.
Sow-thistle, Marsh   Sonchus palustris
  Perennial   arvensis
  Prickly   asper
  Smooth   oleraceus

Spearwort, Adder's-tongue Ranunculus ophioglossifolius
  Creeping   reptans
  Greater   lingua
  Lesser   flammula

Speedwell see also Field-s.,
    Water-s.
Speedwell, Alpine   Veronica alpina
  American   peregrina
  Breckland   praecox
  Corsican   repens
  Fingered   triphyllos
  Germander   chamaedrys
  Heath   officinalis
  Ivy-leaved   hederifolia
  Marsh   scutellata
  Rock   fruticans
  Slender   filiformis
  Spiked   spicata
  Spring   verna
  Thyme-leaved   serpyllifolia
  Wall   arvensis
  Wood   montana

Spider-orchid, Early   Ophrys sphegodes
  Late   fuciflora

Spignel   Meum athamanticum

Spike-rush, Common   Eleocharis palustris
  Dwarf   parvula
  Few-flowered   quinqueflora
  Many-stalked   multicaulis
  Needle   acicularis
  Northern   austriaca
  Slender   uniglumis

Spindle   Euonymus europaeus

Spleenwort, Alternate-leaved Asplenium x alternifolium
  Black   adiantum-nigrum
  Forked   septentrionale
  Green   viride
  Irish   onopteris
  Lanceolate   billotii
  Maidenhair   trichomanes
  Sea   marinum

<u>Spotted-orchid, Common</u>

Spotted-orchid, Common	Dactylorhiza fuchsii
Heath	maculata subsp. ericetorum
Springbeauty	Montia perfoliata
Spring-sedge	Carex caryophyllea
Rare	ericetorum
Spruce <u>see also</u> Hemlock-s.	
Spruce, Norway	Picea abies
Sitka	sitchensis
Spurge, Broad-leaved	Euphorbia platyphyllos
Caper	lathyrus
Coral	corallioides
Cypress	cyparissias
Dwarf	exigua
Hairy	villosa
Irish	hyberna
Leafy	esula
Petty	peplus
Portland	portandica
Purple	peplis
Sea	paralias
Sun	helioscopia
Sweet	dulcis
Upright	serrulata
Wood	amygdaloides
Spurge-laurel	Daphne laureola
Spurrey <u>see also</u> Sea-s.	
Spurrey, Corn	Spergula arvensis
Sand	Spergularia rubra
Squill, Autumn	Scilla autumnalis
Spring	verna
Squinancywort	Asperula cynanchica
Dune	occidentalis
Starfruit	Damasonium alisma
Star-of-Bethlehem	Ornithogalum umbellatum
Drooping	nutans
Early	Gagea bohemica
Spiked	Ornithogalum pyrenaicum
Yellow	Gagea lutea
Star-thistle, Lesser	Centaurea diluta
Red	calcitrapa
Rough	aspera
Yellow	solstitialis
Starwort <u>see</u> Water-s.	

Stitchwort, Bog	Stellaria alsine
Greater	holostea
Lesser	graminea
Marsh	palustris
Wood	nemorum
Stock, Hoary	Matthiola incana
Sea	sinuata
Stonecrop, Biting	Sedum acre
Caucasian	spurium
English	anglicum
Hairy	villosum
Mossy	Crassula tillaea
Reflexed	Sedum reflexum
Rock	forsterianum
Tasteless	sexangulare
Thick-leaved	dasyphyllum
White	album
Stork's-bill, Common	Erodium cicutarium subsp.
	cicutarium
Musk	moschatum
Sea	maritimum
Sticky	cicutarium subsp. bipinnatum
Strapwort	Corrigiola litoralis
Strawberry, Barren	Potentilla sterilis
Garden	Fragaria x ananassa
Hautbois	moschata
Wild	vesca
Yellow-flowered	Duchesnea indica
Strawberry-blite	Chenopodium capitatum
Strawberry-tree	Arbutus unedo
Succory, Lamb's	Arnoseris minima
Sundew, Great	Drosera anglica
Oblong-leaved	intermedia
Round-leaved	rotundifolia
Sunflower	Helianthus annuus
Sweet-briar	Rosa rubiginosa
Small-flowered	micrantha
Small-leaved	agrestis
Sweet-flag	Acorus calamus
Sweet-grass, Floating	Glyceria fluitans
Hybrid	x pedicellata
Plicate	plicata
Reed	maxima

Sweet-grass, Small

Sweet-grass - continued
  Small   Glyceria declinata

Sweet-William   Dianthus barbatus

Swine-cress   Coronopus squamatus
  Lesser   didymus

Sycamore   Acer pseudoplatanus

Tamarisk   Tamarix gallica

Tansy   Tanacetum vulgare

Tapegrass   Vallisneria spiralis

Tare, Hairy   Vicia hirsuta
  Slender   tenuissima
  Smooth   tetrasperma

Tasselweed, Beaked   Ruppia maritima
  Spiral   cirrhosa

Tea see Labrador-t.

Teaplant, China   Lycium chinense
  Duke of Argyll's   barbarum

Tear-thumb, American   Polygonum sagittatum

Teasel   Dipsacus fullonum subsp.
                                     sylvestris
  Fuller's   fullonum subsp. fullonum
  Small   pilosus
  Yellow-flowered   strigosus

Thistle see also Blue-sow-t.,
    Sow-t., Star-t.
Thistle, Cabbage   Cirsium oleraceum
  Carline   Carlina vulgaris
  Cotton   Onopordum acanthium
  Creeping   Cirsium arvense
  Dwarf   acaule
  Marsh   palustre
  Meadow   dissectum
  Melancholy   helenioides
  Milk   Silybum marianum
  Musk   Carduus nutans
  Plymouth   pycnocephalus
  Slender   tenuiflorus
  Spear   Cirsium vulgare
  Tuberous   tuberosum
  Welted   Carduus acanthoides

Thistle - continued
  Woolly   Cirsium eriophorum

Thorn-apple   Datura stramonium

Thorow-wax   Bupleurum rotundifolium
  False   subovatum

Thrift   Armeria maritima subsp.
                                 maritima
  Jersey   alliacea
  Tall   maritima subsp. elongata

Thyme, Basil   Acinos arvensis
  Breckland   Thymus serpyllum
  Large   pulegioides
  Wild   praecox subsp. arcticus

Timothy   Phleum pratense subsp.
                                 pratense

Toadflax see also Bastard-t.
Toadflax, Common   Linaria vulgaris
  Ivy-leaved   Cymbalaria muralis
  Jersey   Linaria pelisseriana
  Pale   repens
  Prostrate   supina
  Purple   purpurea
  Sand   arenaria
  Small   Chaenorhinum minus

Toothwort   Lathraea squamaria
  Purple   clandestina

Tor-grass   Brachypodium pinnatum

Tormentil   Potentilla erecta
  Trailing   anglica

Traveller's-joy   Clematis vitalba

Tree see Strawberry-t.,
    Wayfaring-t.

Tree-mallow   Lavatera arborea
  Smaller   cretica

Tree-of-Heaven   Ailanthus altissima

Trefoil see also Bird's-foot-t.
Trefoil, Hop   Trifolium campestre
  Large   aureum
  Lesser   dubium
  Slender   micranthum

Tufted-sedge

Tufted-sedge	Carex elata
Slender	acuta
Tulip, Wild	Tulipa sylvestris
Turnip, Wild	Brassica rapa
Tussock-sedge, Fibrous	Carex appropinquata
Greater	paniculata
Lesser	diandra
Tutsan	Hypericum androsaemum
Stinking	hircinum
Tall	inodorum
Twayblade, Common	Listera ovata
Lesser	cordata
Twinflower	Linnaea borealis

Valerian, Common	Valeriana officinalis
Marsh	dioica
Pyrenean	pyrenaica
Red	Centranthus ruber
Venus's-looking-glass	Legousia hybrida
Vernal-grass, Annual	Anthoxanthum aristatum
Sweet	odoratum
Veronica, Hedge	Hebe x franciscana
Vervain	Verbena officinalis

Vetch see also Bitter-v.,
    Milk-v., Yellow-v.

Vetch, Bithynian	Vicia bithynica
Bush	sepium
Common	sativa subsp. sativa
Crown	Coronilla varia
Fine-leaved	Vicia tenuifolia
Fodder	villosa*
Horseshoe	Hippocrepis comosa
Kidney	Anthyllis vulneraria
Narrow-leaved	Vicia sativa subsp. nigra
Spring	lathyroides
Tufted	cracca
Wood	sylvatica
Vetchling, Grass	Lathyrus nissolia
Hairy	hirsutus
Meadow	pratensis
Yellow	aphaca

Vine see Grape-v., Russian-v.

Violet see also Dame's-v.,
    Dog-v., Water-v.
Violet, Fen   Viola persicifolia
  Hairy   hirta
  Marsh   palustris
  Sweet   odorata
  Teesdale   rupestris

Viper's-bugloss   Echium vulgare
  Purple   plantagineum

Viper's-grass   Scorzonera humilis

Wallflower   Cheiranthus cheiri

Wall-rocket, Annual   Diplotaxis muralis
  Perennial   tenuifolia

Wall-rue   Asplenium ruta-muraria

Walnut   Juglans regia

Warty-cabbage   Bunias orientalis
  Southern   erucago

Water-cress   Nasturtium officinale
  Fool's   Apium nodiflorum
  Hybrid   Nasturtium x sterile
  Narrow-fruited   microphyllum

Water-crowfoot, Brackish   Ranunculus baudotii
  Common   aquatilis
  Fan-leaved   circinatus
  Pond   peltatus
  River   fluitans
  Stream   penicillatus
  Thread-leaved   trichophyllus

Water-dropwort, Corky-fruited   Oenanthe pimpinelloides
  Fine-leaved   aquatica
  Hemlock   crocata
  Narrow-leaved   silaifolia
  Parsley   lachenalii
  River   fluviatilis
  Tubular   fistulosa

Water-lily, Fringed   Nymphoides peltata
  Hybrid   Nuphar x intermedia
  Least   pumila
  White   Nymphaea alba
  Yellow   Nuphar lutea

Water-milfoil, Alternate	Myriophyllum alterniflorum
Spiked	spicatum
Whorled	verticillatum
Water-parsnip, Greater	Sium latifolium
Lesser	Berula erecta
Water-pepper	Polygonum hydropiper
Small	minus
Tasteless	mite
Water-plantain	Alisma plantago-aquatica
Floating	Luronium natans
Lesser	Baldellia ranunculoides
Narrow-leaved	Alisma lanceolatum
Ribbon-leaved	gramineum
Water-purslane	Lythrum portula
Water-soldier	Stratiotes aloides
Water-speedwell, Blue	Veronica anagallis-aquatica
Pink	catenata
Water-starwort, Autumnal	Callitriche hermaphrodita
Blunt-fruited	obtusangula
Common	stagnalis
Intermediate	hamulata
Pedunculate	brutia
Short-leaved	truncata
Various-leaved	platycarpa
Water-violet	Hottonia palustris
Waterweed, Canadian	Elodea canadensis
Curly	Lagarosiphon major
Large-flowered	Egeria densa
Nuttall's	Elodea nuttallii
South American	callitrichoides
Waterwort, Eight-stamened	Elatine hydropiper
Six-stamened	hexandra
Wax see Thorow-w.	
Wayfaring-tree	Viburnum lantana
Weld	Reseda luteola
Wheat see Cow-w.	
Whin, Petty	Genista anglica
Whitebeam, Broad-leaved	Sorbus latifolia*

* These Whitebeams comprise some closely allied species, most of which require expert determination. If this has been made it should be so indicated.

114

Whitebeam - continued
  Common
  Rock
  Swedish

Whitlowgrass, Common
  Hoary
  Rock
  Round-podded
  Wall
  Yellow

Whorl-grass

Wild-oat
  Winter

Willow, Almond
  Bay
  Bedford
  Crack
  Creeping
  Cricket-bat
  Dark-leaved
  Downy
  Dwarf
  Eared
  Goat
  Golden
  Grey
  Mountain
  Net-leaved
  Purple
  Rusty
  Tea-leaved
  Welsh
  White
  Whortle-leaved
  Woolly

Willowherb, Alpine
  American
  Broad-leaved
  Chickweed
  Great
  Hoary
  Marsh
  New Zealand
  Pale
  Rosebay
  Short-fruited
  Spear-leaved
  Square-stalked

Winter-cress
  American
  Medium-flowered

Sorbus aria
  rupicola
  intermedia

Erophila verna
Draba incana
  norvegica
Erophila spathulata
Draba muralis
  aizoides

Catabrosa aquatica

Avena fatua
  sterilis subsp. ludoviciana

Salix triandra
  pentandra
  fragilis var. russelliana
  fragilis var. fragilis
  repens
  alba var. caerulea
  myrsinifolia
  lapponum
  herbacea
  aurita
  caprea
  alba var. vitellina
  cinerea subsp. cinerea
  arbuscula
  reticulata
  purpurea
  cinerea subsp. oleifolia
  phylicifolia
  fragilis var. decipiens
  alba var. alba
  myrsinites
  lanata

Epilobium anagallidifolium
  ciliatum
  montanum
  alsinifolium
  hirsutum
  parviflorum
  palustre
  brunnescens
  roseum
Chamerion angustifolium
Epilobium obscurum
Epilobium lanceolatum
  tetragonum

Barbarea vulgaris
  verna
  intermedia

Winter-cress - continued
Small-flowered   Barbarea stricta

Wintergreen, Chickweed   Trientalis europaea
    Common   Pyrola minor
    Intermediate   media
    One-flowered   Moneses uniflora
    Round-leaved   Pyrola rotundifolia
    Serrated   Orthilia secunda

Wireplant   Muehlenbeckia complexa

Woad   Isatis tinctoria

Woodruff   Galium odoratum
    Pink   Asperula taurina

Wood-rush, Curved   Luzula arcuata
    Fen   pallescens
    Field   campestris
    Great   sylvatica
    Hairy   pilosa
    Heath   multiflora
    Snow-white   nivea
    Southern   forsteri
    Spiked   spicata
    White   luzuloides

Wood-sedge   Carex sylvatica
    Starved   depauperata
    Thin-spiked   strigosa

Woodsia, Alpine   Woodsia alpina
    Oblong   ilvensis

Wood-sorrel   Oxalis acetosella

Wormwood   Artemisia absinthium
    Field   campestris
    Sea   maritima

Woundwort, Downy   Stachys germanica
    Field   arvensis
    Hedge   sylvatica
    Limestone   alpina
    Marsh   palustris

Yarrow   Achillea millefolium

Yellow-cress, Austrian   Rorippa austriaca
    Creeping   sylvestris
    Great   amphibia
    Marsh   palustris
    Northern   islandica

Yellow-eyed-grass	Sisyrinchium californicum

Yellow-rattle
  Greater
	Rhinanthus minor
	  angustifolius

Yellow-sedge, Common
  Large
  Long-stalked
  Small-fruited
	Carex demissa
	  flava
	  lepidocarpa
	  serotina

Yellow-sorrel, Least
  Procumbent
  Upright
	Oxalis exilis
	  corniculata
	  europaea

Yellow-vetch
  Hairy
	Vicia lutea
	  hybrida

Yellow-wort	Blackstonia perfoliata
Yew	Taxus baccata
Yorkshire-fog	Holcus lanatus